P9-CDP-908

FLASH!

SEEING THE UNSEEN BY ULTRA-HIGH SPEED PHOTOGRAPHY

flash!

SEEING THE UNSEEN BY ULTRA HIGH-SPEED PHOTOGRAPHY

BY

HAROLD E. EDGERTON

AND

JAMES R. KILLIAN, Jr.

HALE, CUSHMAN & FLINT
Boston

First printing, October, 1939

PRINTED IN THE UNITED STATES OF AMERICA

BY THE ADAMS PRESS, INC., LEXINGTON, MASS.

CONTENTS

Kick-Off . . . . Frontispiece

The Meaning of the Pictures

Exploring the World of Time and Motion 9

Living Motion 25

The Turtle Dove 27

The Homing Pigeon 28

Quick as a Hummingbird 30

Acrobats (Parlor Tumblers) 33

"Filmy Shapes that Haunt the Dusk" (Bats) 37

Where the Bee Sucks 40

Assorted Insects 41

The Flight of Insects 42

Details of a Cat Lapping 44

Bullets in Action 45

Four Stages in the Firing of an Old Revolver 46

Firing a Mauser Automatic 48

A Shotgun Is Fired 50

Collision at 1,800 Miles Per Hour! 52

This Has Never Been Seen Before 54

Sports 55

Golf

When the Ball Is Struck 56

Multiple 1/100,000-Second Exposures of Golf Strokes 58

Catching the Click 61

Bobby Jones 64

Densmore Shute 69

Ralph Guldahl 70

Roland Wingate 72

James Thomson: How He Drives 74

The Bird Turns (Badminton) 80

Tennis 81
John Bromwich 83
Charles Hare 86
300 Pictures a Second 88
The Swirls and Eddies of a Stroke 89
Yvon Petra 90
Virginia Wolfenden 91
Robert L. Riggs, Jr., in Action 92
Squash 94
Table Tennis 96
Baseball 97
Placement Kicks 102
Fencing 104
Archery 108
Lacrosse 111
Indian Clubs 113
Drops and Splashes 116
Birth of a Bubble 116
A Falling Drop of Milk 118
Drop Falling into Reservoir of Milk 120
Drop of Milk Splashing on a Plate 122
Coronet 123
Formation of a Drop, I 124
Formation of a Drop, II 125
Long-Distance Drops 127
In a Shot Tower 128
Water Knife 129
Ginger Ale 130
Soda Water 131
A Stream Is a Series of Drops 132
Lawn Sprinkler 134
Garden Hose 134
What Is It? 135
This Is Coffee 136
This Is Milk 137
The Tumbling Cup 138
Water Wheel 139
Soap Bubbles 140

In the Service of Science and Industry 143
The Fan Is Turning 2,000 Revolutions a Minute 142
Ship's Propeller 143
Into the Human Throat with the High-Speed Camera 144
Spinning 146
At 10,000 R.P.M. 147
Weaving 148
The Prop Bends 149
How Fast Does Glass Crack? 150
Seeing the Strains in Cracking Glass 153
Ultraspeed Motion Pictures 156
Quenching 158
Even the Clam 161
Graphical Analysis of Machine Operation 162
High-Speed Operations Stand Still for Observation 163
People in Action 164
Skipping Rope 166
Boy Jumping 168
Fanning Cards 169
Levitation 170
Play 171
Frozen Motion 173
Flowing Motion 174
Jump 175
The Dance 176
Portraits 178
The Iris of the Eye 181
Quick as a Wink 182
Faces and Muscles in Action 183
Jujitsu—with Expression 186
Falling Cat 188
Schooling Greyhound 188
Perfect Form 190
Dog and Mouse 191
Shower Bath 192
Bedtime 193
Directions for Assembling a Flash Unit 194
Acknowledgments 197
Selected References 199

THE MEANING OF THE PICTURES

EXPLORING THE WORLD OF TIME AND MOTION

A SCIENTIFIC wag once sought to throw new light on the theory of relativity with this happy Limerick:

There was a young lady named Bright
Whose speed was faster than light;
    She eloped on a day
    In a relative way,
And returned on the previous night.

Obviously such a fast young lady was not to be seen; her elopement was too rapid for man's eye to see and her time too capricious for him to follow.

Now this japery is not all jest. Modern science has taught us strange things about time and described concepts of space startlingly different from that presented in our high-school textbooks. Even in the world as we normally know it, science has called our attention to the unseen and unknown, and enabled us to see and understand by contracting and expanding not only space but time.

In doing so the scientist and engineer have had to devise accessories for the human eye. Although remarkable as an optical instrument, the eye has at least one profound limitation—its inability to see rapidly moving objects. The unaided eye, cannot, for example, see a bullet in flight, the way a falling cat turns to land on its feet, the distortion in the rotor of a spinning motor, or the beautiful coronet-like splashes of a raindrop falling in a pool. It cannot ever, as Dr. Irving Langmuir recently demonstrated, see a deer fly cruising along at the 800-miles-per-hour speed claimed for it by some naturalists. By whirling a pellet of lead, the size of a deer fly, on the end of a string, Dr. Langmuir found that at 13 miles per hour the fly was only a blur, at 26 miles per hour it was barely visible as a moving object, at 43 miles per hour it appeared as a very faint line and its direction could not be recognized, while at 64 miles per hour and faster it was wholly invisible. Little wonder that we fail to see a bullet traveling 1,800 miles per hour.

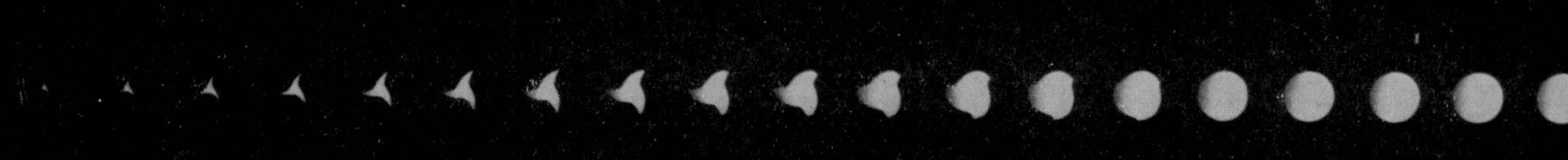

A MECHANICAL SHUTTER IN ACTION

A series of pictures, taken at the rate of 4,200 per second, on a high-grade mechanical shutter set

Beyond the horizon of human vision lies a whole world of such unseen rapid motion. It surrounds us in our everyday life, and we are unable to penetrate it just as, before the telescope and the microscope, we were unable to break through the barriers of space and see the mountains and craters of the moon, or the germs that make us ill and the micro-organisms that make our wine.

To enter this absorbing world of motion, the eye must have an accessory that will manipulate time as the microscope manipulates space—that will, moreover, harness time to space visually. Not until the development of photography and the stroboscope did this feat of legerdemain become feasible and not until the invention of high-speed stroboscopic or single-flash photography—to which this book is devoted—was it achieved.

Both photographic and mechanical factors make it impossible for an unaided camera with a mechanical shutter to take pictures at the speeds used in taking the photographs presented in this book. High-speed photography shows the conventional camera to be a laggard, as demonstrated by the picture above of an ordinary shutter opening and closing.

High speed properly describes single-exposure cameras that take photographs with exposures shorter than 1/10,000 of a second, and motion-picture cameras that operate at speeds in excess of 300 pictures (frames) per second (the motion-picture camera normally operates at 16 to 24 frames per second). Most of the pictures in this book were taken with exposures shorter than 1/50,000 of a second, and motion pictures have been taken at a rate as high as 6,000 per second. In the laboratory at the Massachusetts Institute of Technology, where these pictures were made, an exposure of 1/100,000 of a second has become commonplace, and the unimaginable interval of 1/1,000,000 of a second has become thoroughly domesticated and broken to harness as a useful part of the time scale. A millionth of a second exposure! Let us represent, figuratively, one second by the distance—about 3,000 miles— from New York to San Francisco.

to give an exposure of 1/200th of a second. Thirty-nine pictures were taken between the start and the finish of this exposure. They show that the shutter was "wide open" only 8/4,200ths of a second.

Then a millionth of a second is the distance across your living room, say about 15 feet. It makes that old expression, "quick as a wink," seem absurdly gross, for high-speed pictures of the eye show that the average man or woman takes the interminably long time of 1/40 of a second to wink once. On the other hand, if we are to investigate the private life of a rifle bullet traveling at 2,700 feet per second, or 1,800 miles per hour, a millionth of a second is not too brief an exposure.

Such speeds are necessary, then, to capture ultrarapid motion. As an illustration, take a golf ball zooming away after an average drive. An ordinary camera, with its shutter set at 1/1,000 of a second, would photograph the traveling golf ball as a blur about two inches long. The exposure time must be far less than 1/1,000 of a second in order to produce a sharp, clear photograph of the ball. It must be shorter than 1/100,000 of a second. So far no practical mechanical shutter has yet been built to perform as fast as this. Furthermore, if it could be constructed, there would still remain the almost insuperable problem of obtaining sufficient light to expose the film in so short a time as 1/100,000 of a second.

Shutters, therefore, are not used to take the kind of high-speed pictures shown in this book. Instead, electrical control of the illumination replaces shutters. The light is turned on only when a picture is to be exposed, in a fashion similar to taking photographs with photoflash bulbs, except that the duration of the flash of a flash bulb is some 2,500 times longer than the 1/100,000 of a second maximum exposure necessary for "freezing" the golf ball. The flash of the light is substituted for the opening and closing of a shutter. This does not mean that an ordinary camera cannot be used to take high-speed pictures (all the pictures in this book were taken with standard cameras); it means that the exposure is provided by a light flashing on and off quicker than any shutter can open and close.

Professor Edgerton and his associates, Messrs. Germeshausen and Grier, have designed lighting equipment for giving either a single flash for taking a single "still" picture, or a series of flashes with a predetermined interval of time between them for taking a single multiple-exposure photograph and motion pictures. Whether there is a single flash or a succession of flashes, the light is produced by an electric spark—miniature lightning—inside a gas-filled lamp. Electricity flows into a kind of electrical reservoir known as a condenser, and when the reservoir is full, it overflows at the desired instant to produce a brilliant flash inside the lamp. Electrical controls make it possible to govern very accurately the time between flashes, and the exact moment of flash. To take one of the bullet pictures shown on page 46 required a single flash lasting about 1/1,000,000 of a second. To take motion pictures of a pistol like the sequences shown on page 157, the light was turned on and off at a frequency of 600 flashes per second, and each flash lasted for 5/1,000,000 of a second.

The flashing lamp, which is the heart of the Edgerton system of speed photography, has another important quality. It produces a light of great actinic intensity and many times more brilliant than sunlight, as of course it must if the exposures used are to yield good pictures. Even though the eye seeing it is unaware of unusual brightness, the instantaneous intensity of each flash exceeds the light of approximately 40,000 50-watt bulbs such as are used in household lighting. This intense illumination allows photographic exposures to be made at small apertures, **f**:11 or less. With this equipment the taking of speed photographs becomes relatively simple. Any standard camera and lens equipment may be used to get effective exposures up to 1/1,000,000 of a second, and special fast emulsions are not necessary although they are, of course, useful. Moreover, the pictures so obtained are true reflected-light photographs with good depth and detail.

The method of taking "still" pictures of moving objects with a single flash of light is not new; it is almost as old as photography itself even though it is only now coming into wide use. William Henry Fox Talbot, who shares with Daguerre the honor of taking the first photographs ever made and who discovered the calotype process and the negative-positive technique, patented a method of instantaneous photography in 1851. In a darkened room he focused a camera on a rapidly revolving disk, and by means of an electric spark produced by the discharge of a Leyden battery he obtained an unblurred picture of a clipping from the London "Times" which was attached to the revolving disk.

After Talbot, spark photography was developed to a high state of perfection by Mach, Cranz, Boys, and others, particularly for photographing bullets in silhouette (see page 45). One advantage of these silhouette spark pictures is that they show the shadows of the sound waves produced by the bullets. These waves become visible because changes produced by the bullets in the density of the air vary the refractive index.

The older spark method, however, is complex, of value mainly for silhouettes, and limited almost entirely to the laboratory. Dr. Edgerton, by utilizing electronic devices developed in recent years, has been able to substitute for the electric spark a tube or lamp with a control circuit which provides adequate illumination for reflected-light photographs. Other experiments with electrical discharge photography are listed in the bibliography.

THE photographs in this book are mainly single-flash pictures, but Dr. Edgerton's lights will also flash successively at a controlled rate and can be used to view rapid motion directly with the eye, to take multiple exposures, or to take motion pictures. Such a pulsing light is technically called a stroboscope (a word meaning, roughly, "whirling watcher").

A common illustration of stroboscopic seeing is the use of a flashing light to read letters painted on the blades of a revolving electric fan. Suppose the fan is turning 18 revolutions per second. Seen in ordinary light it looks like a whirling disk because the eye is too slow to pick out the separate blades and therefore sees only a blur, just as the ordinary camera blurs the golf ball. But examine the rotating fan under stroboscopic light flashing at the same rate (18 times a second), and the eye sees the fan apparently standing still, and the printing can be read.

Not only can the fan be made to "stand still"; it can be viewed in slow motion, although its actual speed is still 18 revolutions per second. Regulate the stroboscopic light to 16 flashes per second and the fan will appear to be turning only two revolutions per second (the difference between 18 and 16). Speed up the flashing rate of the light beyond the speed of the fan and the fan will appear to turn slowly backwards.

In relation to our own arbitrary scale, time is thus juggled, slowed, frozen, or reversed by the stroboscope. From a realm never entered by the eye it is transposed into the eye's own sluggish world.

The stroboscope in its original form was not a flashing light; it was a disk, with alternate open and closed areas, which, when revolving, gave an intermittent view of a moving object or series of objects. The reader can easily construct this simple mechanical "whirling watcher" himself. Cut a disk from a large piece of cardboard and near its rim cut a series of slots equally spaced and large enough to look through when held close to the eye. From the center of the disk draw radial lines, extending from the center like the spokes of a wheel, one line for each slot. Then mount the disk so that it may be held vertically and revolved rapidly. Now hold the disk before a mirror so that you can look through a slot and see the image of the radial lines in the mirror. When you set the disk spinning and look through the successive openings provided by the slots, you will see in the mirror not the blur you would normally see, but the image of each radial line distinct and standing still.

The explanation of this illusion is simple if we recall that our eyes have a quality known as persistence of vision or "retinal lag." We continue to see an object, line, or light for about one-tenth of a second or less after it has moved away. The four blades of the revolving electric fan, for example, appear as a solid disk because the image of each blade persists in the eye after the blade has moved by.

When we look through the slots of the turning cardboard disk, each slot as it passes the eye gives a glimpse of the image of the disk in the mirror, but the glimpse is so short that the image does not have time to move enough to show any motion. The lines appear to be standing still. When the second slot passes the eye, giving a similar successive view, the first view still persists in the eye and the second merges with it into one single impression. Result: the image continues to stand still.

With this same device we can make the radial lines move slowly forward or slowly backward, just as the electric fan does when the speed of the flashing light is changed and for the same fundamental reason. If we draw more radial lines than there are slots on the disk, we get the first effect of slow forward motion. If there are fewer lines than slots, we see the second effect of slow backward motion, and herein, incidentally, lies the explanation of that illusion we have all seen in the "movies"—an automobile wheel turning backward when the car is clearly moving forward. The intermittent action of the motion-picture camera corresponds to the slots on the disk. If the lines are less numerous than the slots on the disk or if the camera takes pictures at a rate faster than the automobile wheel turns, we receive a view of the next radial line or spoke before it has arrived at the spot where the first was seen, giving the illusion that the first has moved backward slightly.

Here, then, in this simple slotted disk lies the whole secret of the stroboscope, of seeing rapidly moving objects as standing still or in slow motion. A moving image is seen so briefly through a slot or shutter or by the flash of a light that it appears not to move, and this image of nonmotion persists in the eye until the next image replaces it. Of course, it is this physiological quality of persistence of vision that makes the motion picture possible, and the slotted disk—the first stroboscope—was the progenitor of the cinema.

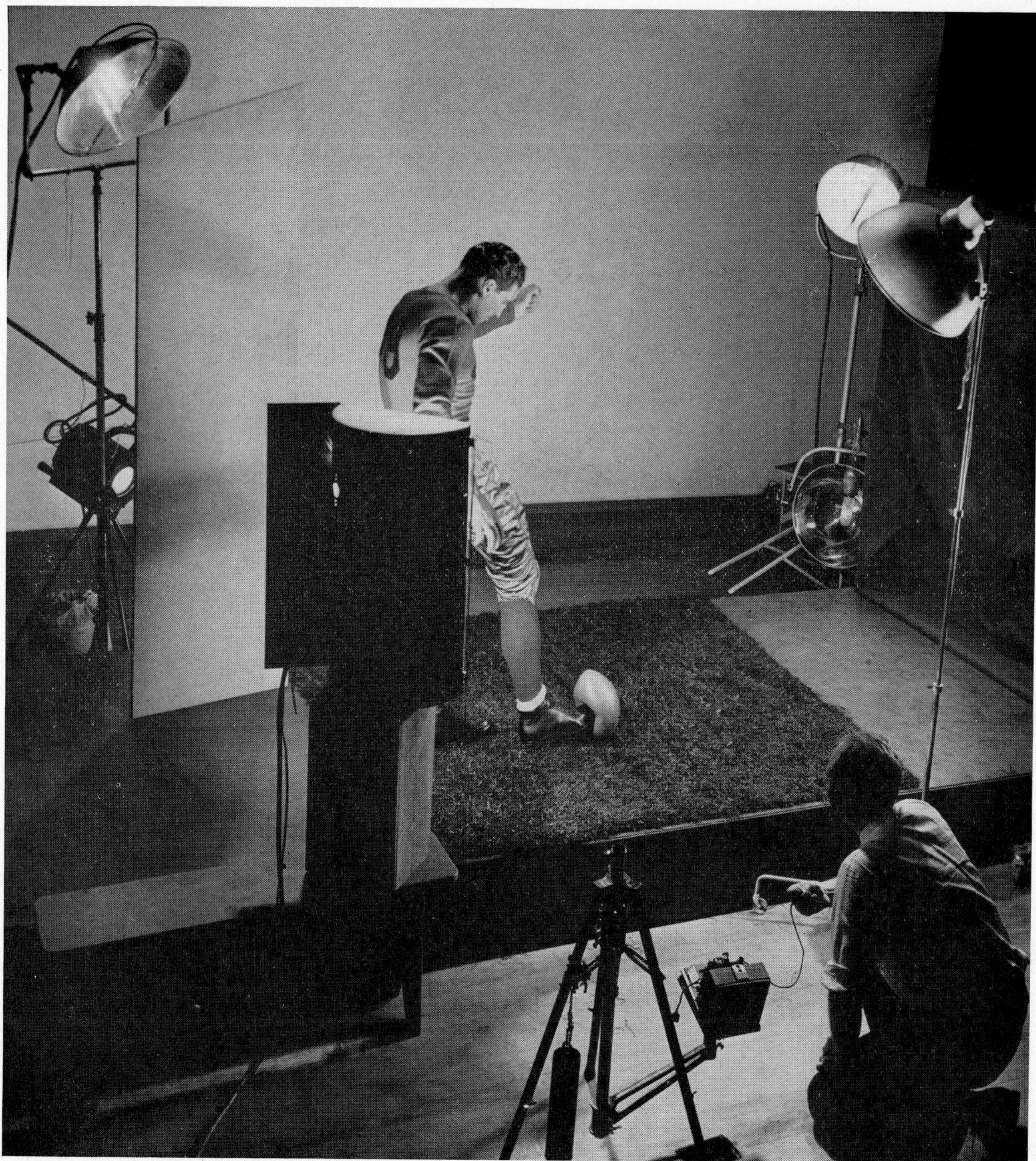

HIGH-SPEED PICTURE OF A HIGH-SPEED PICTURE BEING TAKEN
Here is how the colored frontispiece was staged and lighted in the studio of Gjon Mili, the first professional high-speed photographer. As the lights flash Dr. Edgerton himself releases the shutter during the split-second in which the toe of the kicker bashes in the ball. **For other pictures of kicked footballs see pages 102 and 103.**

The birth of the stroboscope, in 1832, deserves to be remembered. Like many inventions, it was arrived at independently by two men, Plateau of Ghent and Stampfer of Vienna. Both, it seems, were inspired by some investigations of Michael Faraday who, in turn, had probably been prompted to investigate phenomena associated with persistence of vision by observations made by Peter Mark Roget, the British physician who compiled the famous "Thesaurus of English Words and Phrases." Even though Stampfer was a month or so behind Plateau in announcing his invention, the name "stroboscope" which he gave to the device has persisted, probably because Plateau coined for his own apparatus the more formidable term, "phenakistoscope." Plateau made many original contributions to physiological optics, as well as to molecular physics, but the last forty years of his life were spent in complete blindness as a result of his gazing too long at the sun. He lost his own sight, but he helped to give a new vision to mankind!

A CAR MOVING AT APPROXIMATELY 25 MILES PER HOUR

These three pictures reveal, better than any words, the distortion difficulties encountered with a conventional camera when photographing high-speed motion. The first, taken with a focal-plane shutter, shows the distortion in the wheel; the second taken with a Compur shutter at 1/200 of a second, shows the distortion of the spokes. Compare these two with the third taken with the help of Dr. Edgerton's single-flash lamp set to give an exposure of 1/50,000 of a second

It was not long after the invention of the stroboscope that the viewing slots were adapted to the purpose of interrupting a beam of light, thus providing mechanically the periodic flashes that were later to be produced electrically.

Dr. Edgerton's high-speed motion-picture photography, because it uses a controlled, pulsing light, is called Stroboscopic Photography. His contribution has been not only to put the camera and stroboscope into effective double harness but to develop a unique stroboscope which can be controlled and timed accurately and which supplies in readily usable form the brilliant light necessary for photographic use.

He also has overcome the difficulty of flashing the light at the right time, of catching the bullet at the position in which he desires to photograph it or the tennis ball when it is flattened by the racket. This control of the starting time he accomplishes in a variety of ways, depending upon the subject being photographed. Frequently he uses a simple electrical contact actuated by the object itself. For other photographs he lets sound trip his circuit by using a microphone, or he uses a signal produced by the interruption of a beam of light from a photoelectric cell. Much of the success of his pictures derives from these methods of accurately timing the flash that exposes the film.

While no special camera is needed for taking high-speed "still" pictures, high-speed motion pictures require a camera that moves the film fast enough and without any intermittent action. Naturally the faster the action that is being photographed, the faster the camera must be driven. It is impractical, because of mechanical limitations, to drive the usual intermittent motion-picture camera at speeds in excess of about ten times normal, or 240 frames per second. Conventional pictures taken at this increased rate are familiar to all. When they are projected at ordinary speeds, we have "slow-motion" moving pictures which are familiar but always fascinating.

To obtain really high-speed pictures, however, and thereby ultraslow-motion projection, the film must be whipped past the lens at a speed much greater than 240 frames per second. To gain such speed Dr. Edgerton has utilized special cameras that avoid the intermittent film-fed mechanism entirely and use instead a continuously moving film mechanism synchronized with the flashing light. Each time the film has moved the distance occupied by one frame (or by half a frame, if desired), the subject is illuminated by the stroboscope, thus exposing the film. While the film is running, the camera lens remains wide open. The flashing light replaces the shutter action, and its flash is so instantaneous that the racing film has no blurring effect. Normal illumination, such as that encountered indoors, is insufficient to fog the film in these cameras because the film passes the lens so rapidly. When taking 2,000 standard-size pictures a second, the speed of the film approaches 85 miles an hour, which, obviously, means 7,500 feet per minute, or 125 feet per second!

One of the most difficult problems that Dr. Edgerton had to solve in making motion pictures at these speeds was properly to "frame" the pictures so that they might be projected in standard motion-picture equipment. Experts opined that it could not be done. That it has been done will be verified by the many thousands of persons who have viewed the film produced by Dr. Edgerton, entitled "Seeing the Unseen." Available to responsible organizations upon request to the Massachusetts Institute of Technology, this two-reel picture is in constant circulation and has been shown all over the United States. What Dr. Edgerton did was to harness the electrical circuit controlling the light to an accurately constructed contactor driven by the sprocket moving the film. This provided perfect synchronism between the racing film and the flashing light.

The principal limitation of this stroboscopic type of high-speed camera is its inability to record self-luminous subjects such as electric sparks and explosions, and several different systems have been developed to photograph such phenomena. Instead of illuminating the subject for a sufficiently short length of time to avoid blurring, as Edgerton's method does, these systems employ moving optical arrangements which hold the image cast by the lens stationary with respect to a continuously moving film. In other words, by moving a lens, mirror, prism or slit so that the image moves in the direction of the film and with the same velocity, it is possible to take as many as 120,000 pictures a second provided the object being photographed produces sufficient light itself or else can be adequately illuminated. Cameras of this general type, such as those constructed by Jenkins, Thun, Magnan, Suhara, Tuttle, Prince and Rankin, and others, are described in literature listed in the bibliography.

In addition to its capacity to record vagrant and rapid motion, stroboscopic photography is useful for measurement and analysis. Since the interval between flashes may be predetermined, the observer is able to record an action as a function of time. Likewise the distance, velocity, and acceleration of the moving object photographed may be read and calculated from the pictures. To return to the golf ball pictures: It is possible to determine from them the velocities of the ball and the club, as well as the spin of the ball, the angle of departure, and the twist of the club head after it has hit the ball.

The method of measuring the velocities is this: If two very high-speed exposures of a moving object are taken at some small interval apart, the object will have appeared to have moved a short distance. The displacement or motion of the

"IT WORKS!"

One of the earliest (1931) high-speed pictures made with Dr. Edgerton's stroboscope. The motor rotor, upon which the "S" and "N" are painted, was turning at a rate corresponding to a linear speed of 95 miles per hour when the exposure was made. It is Dr. Edgerton himself who watches; the setting is an electrical engineering laboratory at the Massachusetts Institute of Technology

object divided by the interval of time is the average velocity during the interval between the two photographs. Thus if the ball moves two inches in 1/1,000 of a second, then its velocity is 2,000 inches (167 feet) a second. In the multiple-image photographs of golf strokes (pages 58-74) this measurement may be easily made from one photograph. Each image of the club and ball followed the previous one by 1/100 of a second or some other small interval. Knowing this, one readily obtains the duration of the stroke, or any part of it, and the speed of the ball. This ability makes stroboscopic photography a powerful and widely useful tool in scientific research whether that research deals with abstruse laboratory phenomena, the behavior of machinery in a factory, the flight of hummingbirds, or the mechanics of pitching a baseball.

It was Dr. Edgerton's work in electrical measurements that first led him to investigate the stroboscope and the possibility of using it for photography. To use technical terms for a moment, he wished to find a way to measure accurately the angular displacement of the rotor in a synchronous machine. The stroboscope was the most direct and straightforward method of doing this, but with stroboscopes then available, measurements had to be recorded visually, and it was difficult for the observer to catch with accuracy the transient variations in the rotation of the rotor. He therefore set about to design a stroboscopic device that would produce enough light in controlled flashes of sufficiently short duration and of the proper actinic quality to permit a motion-picture record to be made of the turning rotors. His success in developing this stroboscope (first described in the May, 1931, issue of "Electrical Engineering") for this specific purpose led to his subsequent work in high-speed photography and the many improvements he has made.

The present Edgerton stroboscope is by no means confined to the laboratory. In a conveniently portable form it is finding wide use in industry for studying the complexities of high-speed motion either by camera or directly by the eye. Undesirable distortion, irregularities, and vibration in high-speed machinery under the analytical eye of the stroboscope emerge from the blur that normally hides them. The whip of an automobile crankshaft, the shuttle in a high-speed loom, the meshing of gears, and thousands of other motions—rotary, reciprocating, or transient—are brought within the range of the eye to be observed and measured with great precision. Even the psychologists have resorted to high-speed photography to study the behavior response of people to the sound of a pistol shot.

The single-flash type, as it inevitably would be, has been put to work (page 178) by the commercial photographer, who uses it to make portraits as well as action pictures. It gives the photographer a further range, a new mastery of light, and a greater freedom to pursue esthetic objectives. It also serves as a substitute for flash bulbs. The Edgerton lights will flash repeatedly without having to be replaced, although they are not so portable as flash bulbs. The slotted disk of blind Dr. Plateau in its modern electronic version has taken its place in the workaday world.

MUCH fatiguing gibberish has been spoken about the esthetics of photography, and the issue is still joined as to whether photography is, or is not, an art form. Dr. Edgerton as a photographer is first of all a scientist and an electrical engineer, investigating, measuring, seeking new facts about natural phenomena. But there are craftsmanship and esthetic motivation in science, and they inevitably appear in these high-speed pictures. "Science," wrote J. W. N. Sullivan, "is valued for its practical advantages, it is valued because it gratifies disinterested curiosity, and it is valued because it provides the contemplative imagination with objects of great aesthetic charm." These pictures, as scientific records, have the same values, not the least of which is their esthetic charm. They appeal because they bestow comprehension and increase our awareness. They endow us with a new kind of sight that reveals new forms, subtle relationships of time and space, the essence of motion. In the main the esthetic aspects of science are discernible only to the scientist, but here they appear in a universal language for all to appreciate.

As a craftsman Dr. Edgerton is interested not only in facts and analyses but in obtaining a record that presents these facts and analyses in a manner that pleases him. Many times, as in his studies of splashes, he has taken definitive pictures only to discard them because he sought a description that was eloquent as well as lucid. He has photographed drops, birds, bullets, and athletes over and over again to arrive at a satisfying transcription, just as Edward Weston has studied cypress trees and rocks; Edward Steichen, sunflowers; and Alfred Stieglitz, clouds and hands. As an artist does, he has sought to establish the best possible correlation between meaning and expression. And remember that in the split-second realm in which he works, this is the more difficult.

One final word on the relationship of his work to other kinds of photography. It is the genius of photography, as Lewis Mumford has said, to give the "effect of permanence to the transient and ephemeral," and of the motion picture in particular to record movement through both time and space. It is the genius of high-speed still photography to present a dynamic suggestion of motion in a form intermediate between the still and motion picture. And it is the genius of high-speed photography, both still and motion, to reduce and clarify the fuzzy world of the transient and fast. Dr. Edgerton's photographs supply eloquent proof of these abilities. Unretouched as they are without exception, they provide a unique and literal transcript of that time world beyond the threshold of our eyes.

Here, then, in these pictures are not only facts to help us in seeing and doing but new esthetic experiences, new horizons in observation, the stimulation of penetrating a new world of time where the "visual impact of the split second" gives a fresh aspect to the commonplace.

J. R. KILLIAN, JR.

PURPLE FINCH IN FLIGHT
In its beak is a sunflower seed, a favorite food. Note the separation of the wing feathers as the finch executes a downstroke

FEMALE FINCHES FIGHTING

The flight of birds has never been adequately studied and is veiled in controversy. Do birds propel themselves with the upward strokes of their wings as well as with the downward? The French investigator, Etienne Œhmichen, thinks that they do, that the upward stroke utilizes the moving air resulting from the downstroke. Aeronautical engineers are doubtful.

High-speed pictures, still and moving, are helping to answer some of these tantalizing puzzles

LIVING MOTION

Does a trotting horse ever have all four feet off the ground at once? In 1872 this was an agitating question to a group of California sportsmen, for bets had been laid and noses were out of joint over the contradictory answers provided by the unaided eye. When a definitive answer was obtained, not only were bets settled but a long step forward had been taken toward the perfection of motion pictures and the photographic recording of motion.

It was Leland Stanford, railroad magnate and former governor, who hit upon the happy idea that the fledgling art of photography might solve the problem. He sought a photographer and found an Englishman, one Eadweard Muybridge, then plying his trade in California. Muybridge enthusiastically went about photographing a trotting horse and, with a few tantalizing exceptions, consistently missed the horse or drew blank negatives because his method of timing was inadequate and fast emulsions were not then available. Undaunted, Stanford called in one of his engineers, gifted John D. Isaacs, to devise a system of timing, which Isaacs promptly did. With a battery of cameras lined up along a track and with special shutters operated either electrically or by a clock, he made it possible for Muybridge to take a whole series of properly timed instantaneous pictures of the trotting horse. The result was sensational; not only did the pictures show the horse at times with all four feet off the ground but they revealed facts about the locomotion of the horse that left even horse fanciers almost incredulous. Muybridge's career was made, and he spent the rest of his days photographing by this method, all manner of creatures including elephants, asses, hogs, deer, men, baboons, and kangaroos.

When Stanford proudly showed his pictures in Europe and in 1881 sent Muybridge over with others, the pictures served to settle an argument raging among French artists over the attitudes of a running horse, and it was quickly recognized that they could be used in the projecting zoetrope, a device based on Plateau's stroboscope (see page 16) to synthetize the series into an illusion of motion, of a horse actually trotting. More important they came to the attention of Dr. E. J. Marey, physicist and founder of the Marey Institute, who had spent years studying animal motions. He immediately spotted the defect in the Muybridge pictures: When they were viewed in the zoetrope, the horse stayed in the same place and the scenery ran by. He then proceeded to build a photographic "gun," based on a camera built by the astronomer Janssen to record the transit of

Venus, which would take a series of pictures from the same point. After the development of this gun, the motion picture as we know it was just around the corner, awaiting flexible film.

The pictures taken by Muybridge in America and by Marey in France were manna to the eye-hungry people. Artists used them as study material; physiologists, anatomists, and naturalists gained new knowledge from them; and the layman for the first time penetrated the fascinating world that lay beyond the blur of rapid motion.

Not even the coming of the motion picture, however, opened up the entire vista of motion. It remained for high-speed photography in its various forms to remove the blur from very rapid animal motion. The pictures on the preceding and following pages illustrate what now may be accomplished in the perception and analyses of animal motion. Taken at greater and more accurately controlled speeds and showing more detail, they are competent to settle questions more important, perhaps, than bets on the gait of a trotting horse.

THE FINCH COMPLETES ITS UPSTROKE

The downward beat of the dove's wings with the primary feathers bent, unusual in a small bird

The upward beat of the wings. Each primary wing feather acts as a separate airfoil (the technical name for the airplane's wing), the feathers twisting about the long axes of their shafts

The primary feathers are interlocked on the downward beat

The surprising position and contour of the homing pigeon's wings as they start downward

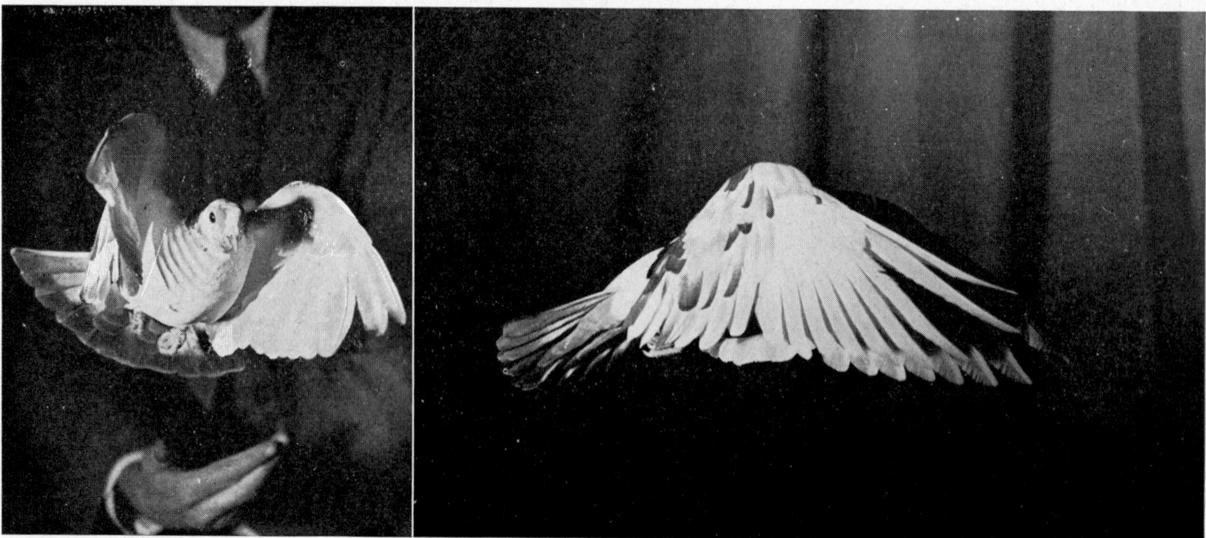

Note shadows of separated primaries on bird's breast

View from the side showing the forward position of the wings. As in the first picture the bird is taking off.

ASCENT

Edward Steichen has made a beautiful combination print of this pose, placing two girls, wonder-eyed, in the lower right corner

QUICK AS A HUMMINGBIRD

At Holderness, N. H., the late Mrs. Laurence J. Webster (above) for many years made her home a sanctuary for ruby-throated hummingbirds. These exquisite creatures, the smallest of American birds, weigh only about one-tenth of an ounce, and in flight their wings beat so rapidly that they appear only as a blur. Mrs. Webster attracted them not only by providing the flowers they love but by placing about her yard brightly colored vials containing sweetened water. So friendly did these birds become that they would feed from her hand.

Efforts to record the flight of the hummingbird with a motion-picture camera resulted only in blurs, as may be seen in the excerpts from the film on page 32. So the stroboscopic camera was taken to Mrs. Webster's home to try its luck. The results are shown on the following three pages. Exposures of 1/100,000 of a second brought the motions of the birds to a dead stop, and high-speed motion pictures taken at 1,000 per second made it possible to measure the frequency of the wing beats. It was found that the wings beat about 60 times a second when the birds are hovering, and the rate increases to about 70 a second when the bird is frightened and flies away.

Hummingbirds are scrappers, and in the picture above two of them are staging a lively fight. This picture is a reproduction from a Kodacrome negative.

THE HUMMINGBIRD'S TONGUE
Here may be seen the tiny tubular tongue protruding from the bill after the bird has fed

PARKED ON EMPTINESS
The bird's tail is a very effective rudder and is in almost continuous movement during hovering

ON THE WING

Above and below. Hummingbirds in movement about their feeding tubes. Their long necks enable them readily to change their center of gravity, which probably explains how they quickly shift the positions of their bodies without altering their wing motion. They frequently maneuver backwards.

Left. An enlargement of three frames from an ordinary motion-picture film taken at the rate of 16 pictures a second. The upper frames show the bird hovering before a feeding tube. In the lower picture the bird turns, and its tail is visible only as a semicircular blur. Contrast these with the high-speed photographs

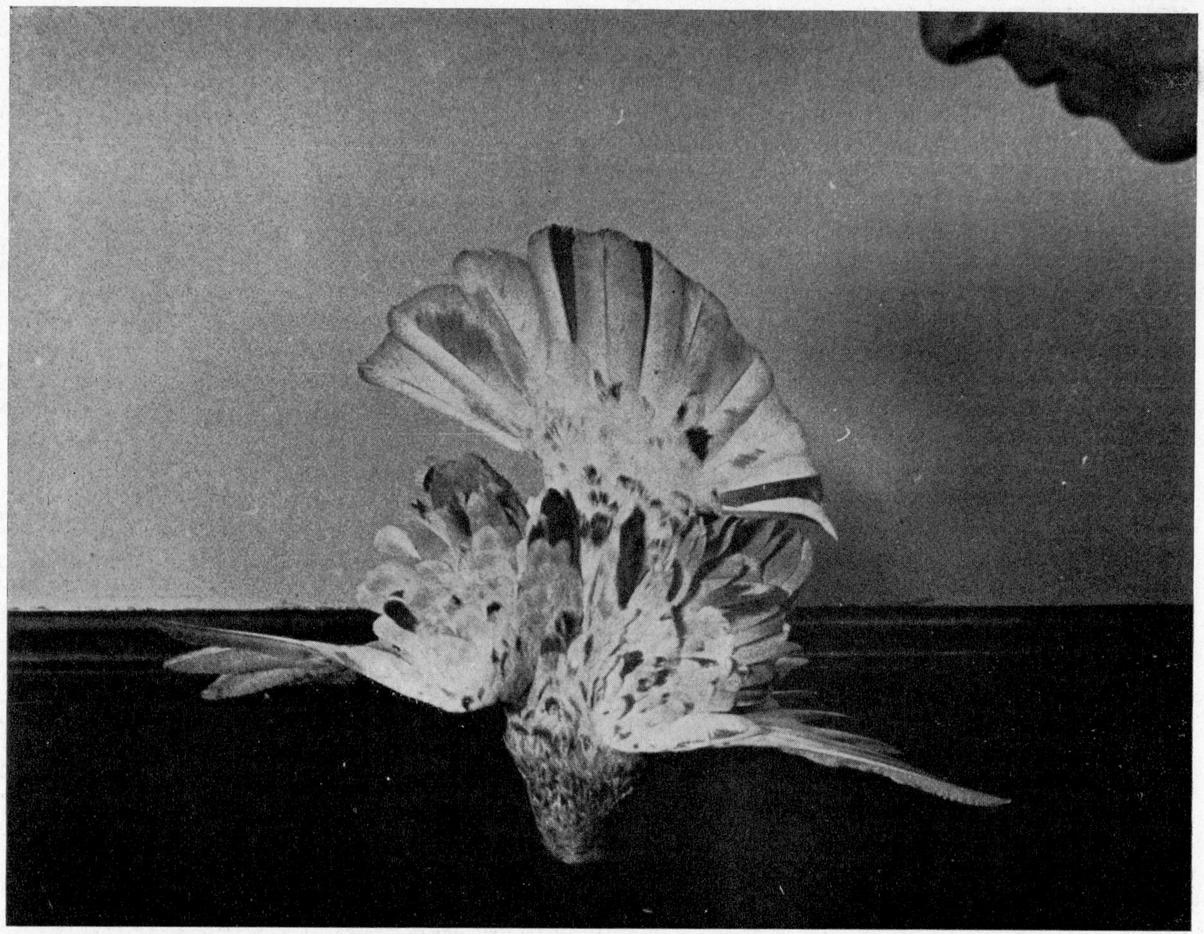

ACROBATS

Exposures: 1/150,000 of A Second

Bred from the air tumbler which loops the loop, the parlor tumbler is a fancy pigeon that has lost the power of flight. Instead of flying, it turns complete backward somersaults. Three types have been developed: one that executes only one somersault, another that invariably turns twice, and a third that stages a whole series of rolls.

In Sumter, S. C., Wendell M. Levi has been working on an encyclopedic book on pigeons, and when he sought detailed pictures of parlor tumblers in action he was stumped; not even his friend, Ray E. Gilbert, who breeds these sports in Salt Lake City, could help him. So Mr. Levi of South Carolina asked Mr. Gilbert of Utah to send some parlor tumblers to Professor Edgerton in Massachusetts to perform before the high-speed camera. Both motion pictures and stills were made, and samples of the latter are shown above and on the next two pages. By this geographical triple play the acrobatics of the parlor tumbler thus became a matter of record for the first time.

HOW A PARLOR TUMBLER TUMBLES

On the opposite page are six stages in the double backward flip of a tumbler. Above is an enlargement of the most striking position

1
2
3
4
5
6

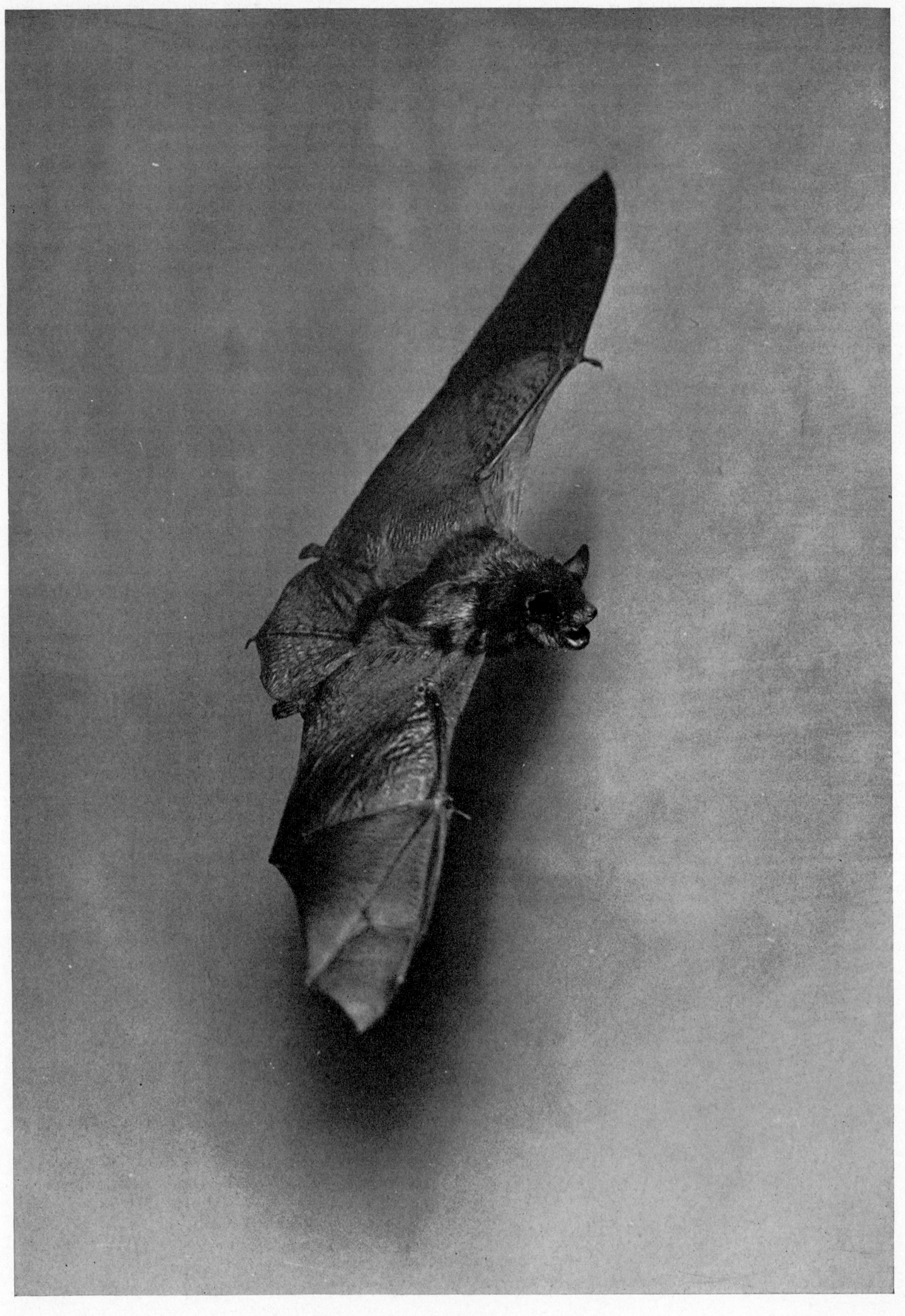

A bat in level flight, showing the membrane that joins the tail and hind legs in use as a horizontal rudder

"FILMY SHAPES THAT HAUNT THE DUSK"

The line is Tennyson's, and he was describing the bat. The adjacent pictures provide documentation for his description, the little brown bat "Myotis Lucifugus Lucifugus", common in New England, being the subject. For a half dozen years Donald R. Griffin, a Harvard student, has been studying these tiny "flying mice," and as a part of his investigation he brought specimens to Edgerton to be photographed. He finds the bats in the dark recesses of old mines and in lonely mountain caves. Bats choose such places for hibernation because they require an even temperature that does not fall below freezing and enough dampness to prevent dehydration.

Bats, maintains Griffin, have been greatly maligned. They do not carry bedbugs, do not get tangled up in women's hair, are not blind, and only the vampire bats of the tropics drink blood. Certainly the bats that posed for these photographs seemed harmless. While they were annoyed by being held, they did no damage since their bite will not break the skin.

Their private lives are interesting. They are mammals, not birds, and their young are born alive. While as many as four may be in a litter, usually only one is born at a time. The mother, in company with other females of the colony, customarily retires to a community maternity ward in a crevice to await the arrival of the young. Baby bats are born with claws fully developed, cling to their mother's fur, and frequently accompany her as a passenger on swift, zigzag flights in pursuit of insects, their chief food.

Stalling to avoid a crash into a wall ahead. The bat uses the membrane between its legs and tail to check its flight

A bat's wings, as these pictures show, are supported by the greatly elongated fingers of its hands, the thumbs of which are hooks. The bat roosts hanging head down by its hind feet, which are used solely for this purpose. Even in death the sharp, curved claws do not relax their secure grip on rock or tree.

Like the homing pigeon (see page 28), bats have a homing instinct, and in studying this mysterious ability Griffin has released bats 65 miles from their roost and found them back there later. There is some evidence that the animals migrate, and Griffin, in co-operation with the United States Biological Survey, has banded thousands. To observe their habits, however, is difficult, for casual observers rarely see them. But in the adjacent pictures is their "cloistered flight" for all to see.

Right. These pictures show a characteristic pose—the open mouth, the bared teeth, the beady eye, the woolly breast

Below. As the bat struggles to escape from the hand, we get a clear view of the structure of its wing, which is a thin membrane stretched between the finger bones of what corresponds to a hand or foot. The thinness of the membrane is apparent; the bones and blood vessels show in silhouette. The "thumb" protruding from the front of the wing is used as a claw or hook

Above and left. The wings in a downward stroke. When flying in the dark, bats rarely strike objects in their paths, probably because their sensitive ears pick up reflected sound. At the left note the banded leg. Griffin, in cooperation with the United States Biological Survey, has banded thousands

Below. This graceful glide shows the whole body, the furry fuselage riding on delicate membrane and slender bone.

WHERE THE BEE SUCKS

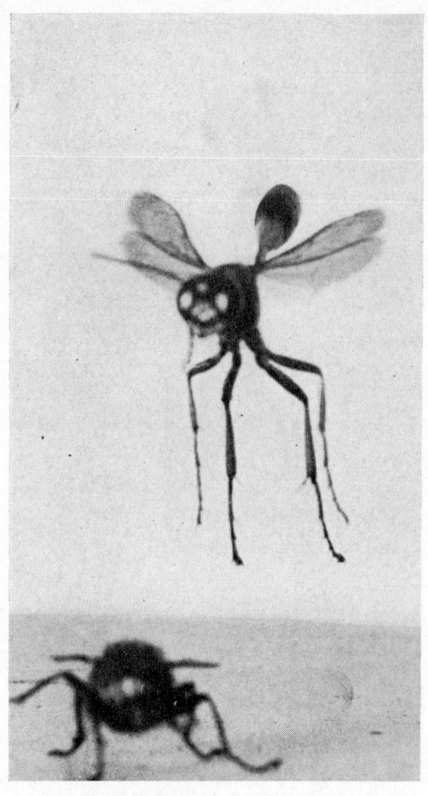

Above. This fly might have been the prototype of the modern pursuit plane. Below. A bumblebee and a wasp perform aerial maneuvers over crawling flies

ASSORTED INSECTS

A ghostly wasp, above, and a shimmering bumblebee, below, contrast grotesque complexity with compact simplicity. The bee's wings seem almost too small and delicate for the buxom body

THE FLIGHT OF INSECTS

The adjacent pictures and those on the preceding two pages are drawn from a series made in collaboration with Leigh E. Chadwick, (see bibliography, page 200) an entomologist, who is studying insect flight

In the adjacent pictures of a dog-day locust in flight, note the highlights caused by the shiny surface of the wings

Beginning the downstroke

The delicate wings and fearsome face of the cicada

Beginning the upstroke

Halfway on the upstroke

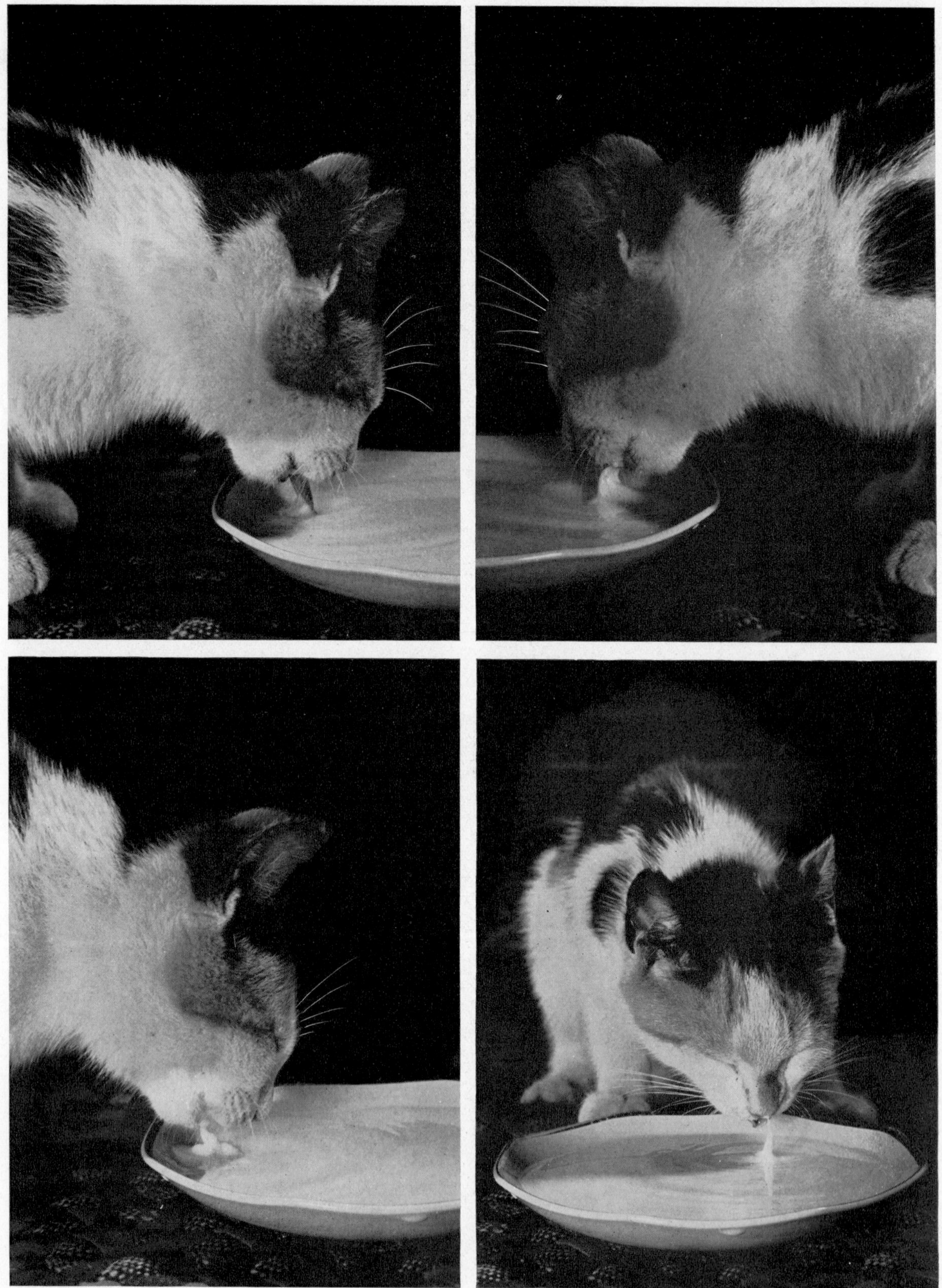

DETAILS OF A CAT LAPPING

. . . in three side views and a front elevation. Apparently the cat's tongue is an effective pumping device. The milk seems to spurt into the mouth like water from a drinking fountain

Silhouette photograph of a .22-caliber, long-rifle bullet in flight, which shows the sound and heat waves set up by the projectile

BULLETS IN ACTION

Many questions about the flight of projectiles remained unanswered until ways to photograph them were devised. Ordnance experts believed for years that bullets continued to gain speed for many feet after they left the muzzle of the gun by the continued pushing effect of the propelling charge in the open air. Silhouette photographs proved conclusively that this acceleration lasts for only a few inches (in the firing of a Springfield rifle, for example). Who has not heard it said that the kick of a pistol affected the accuracy of a shot? Yet photographs show that no uptilting of the gun occurs until the bullet is several feet on its way. Similarly definitive facts have been learned about the leakage of gas around the bullet in the barrel and about the speed of the sound created by the bullet. Until the refinement of stroboscopic photography, bullets could be studied only by shadow, or silhouette, photographs (see above), a method first used by the Austrian physicist Ernst Mach about 1881. In this method the object to be photographed is made to cast a shadow as it passes between an open-air spark and a photographic plate. This method has been of enormous value and will always be used because it is the only one that will record sound waves and turbulence in the air, but it has several limitations. The photography must sometimes be carried out in darkness, the timing of the spark requires complex equipment, and the picture obtained is only an outline, sharp as it may be. With other types of high-speed photography these limitations are avoided, and genuine reflected-light ballistic photographs are possible. For examples of this new achievement in photography, for sharply detailed views of the spectacular events that occur when guns fire and bullets strike, turn the page.

FOUR STAGES IN THE FIRING OF AN OLD REVOLVER

Exposures: 1/1,000,000 of a second at f.11

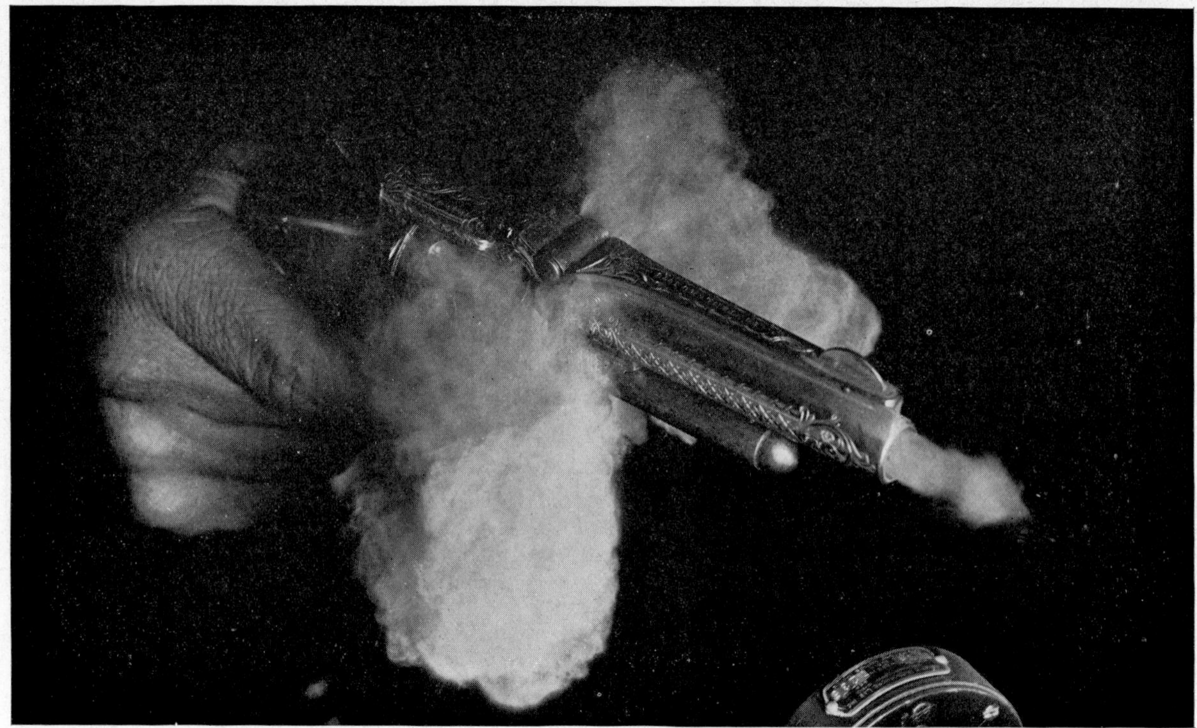

The trigger is pulled, and the action starts. The bullet has not reached the muzzle, and ejected gas is leakage. In ordinary light the gas is hardly visible

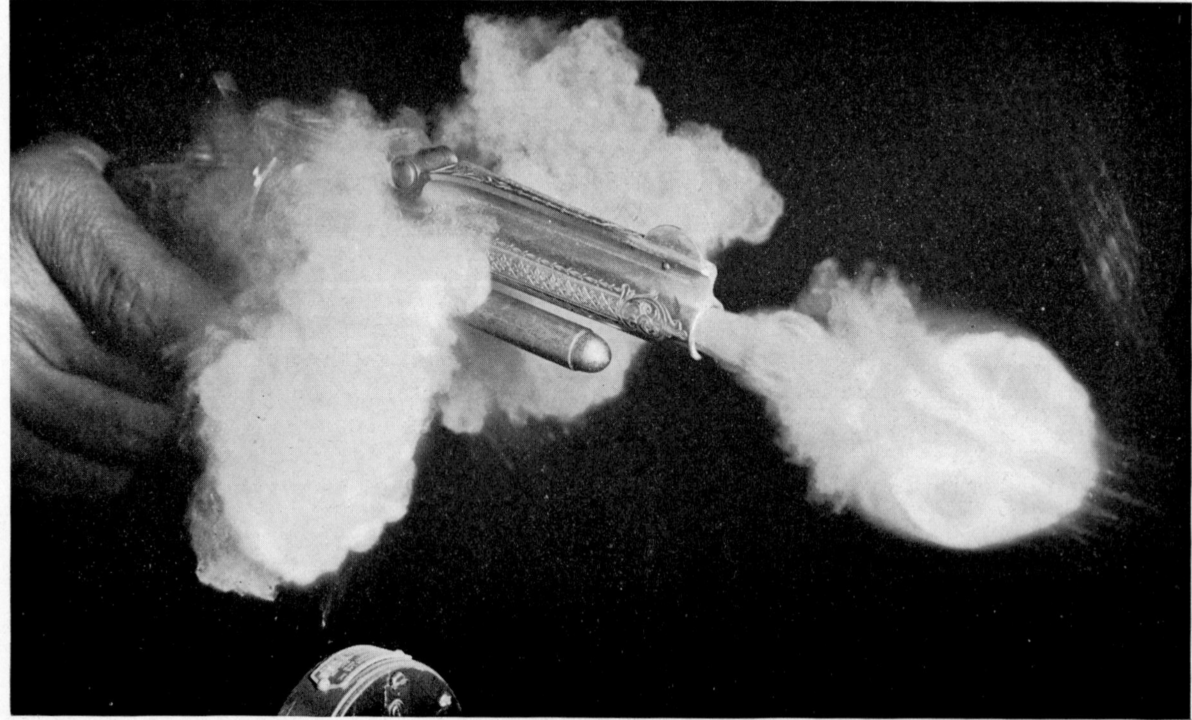

The bullet is out but still surrounded by gas, the propelling charge rushes out of the muzzle, and powder particles from a previous shot are driven ahead of the gas

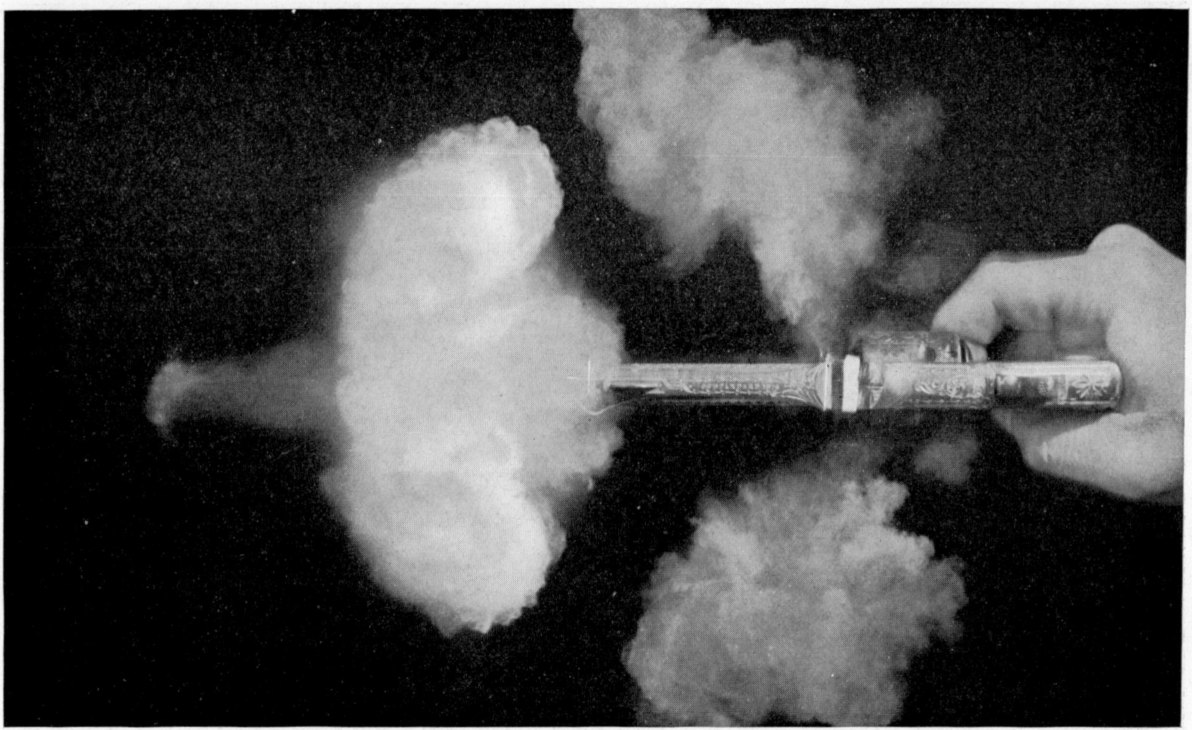

From overhead may be seen the pattern of the smoke which pours out from the back of the barrel and from the muzzle despite the use of smokeless powder

Here the kick of the gun may be seen, occurring after the bullet has outsped the gas. Note clear details on the bullet, the disappearance of the gas that poured from the back of the barrel.

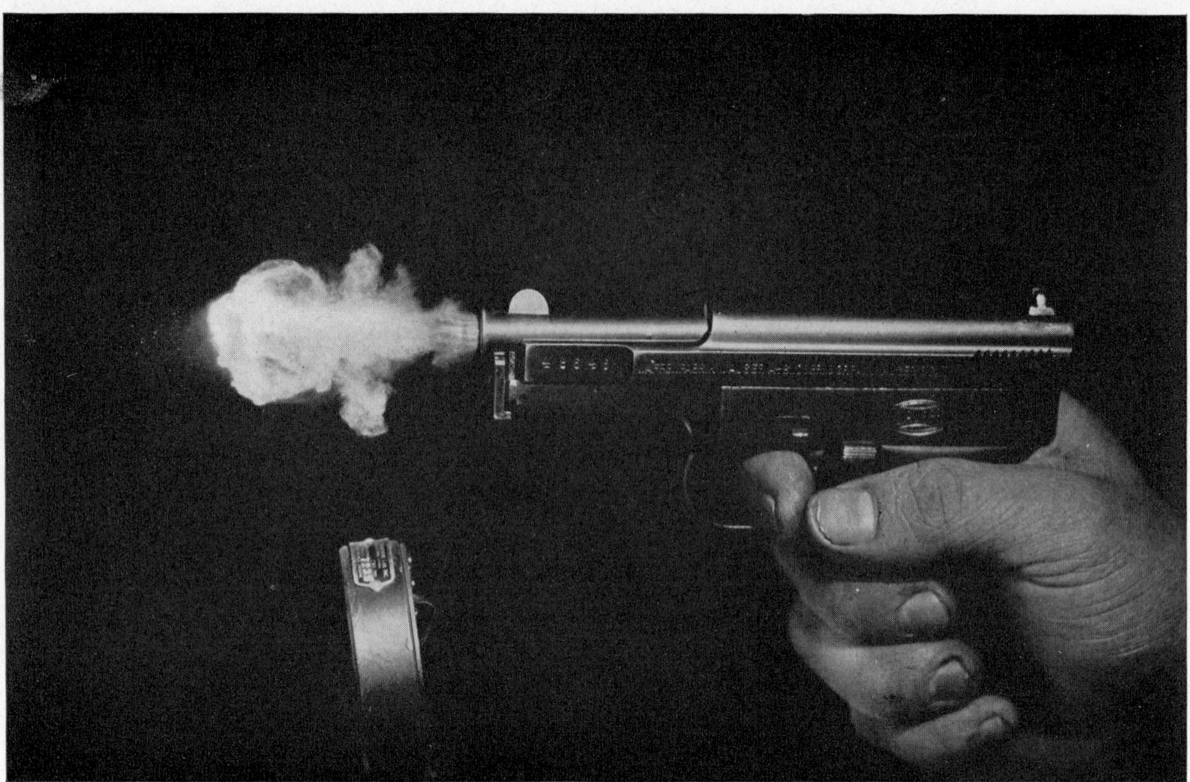

1

FIRING A MAUSER AUTOMATIC

Exposure: 1/1,000,000 of a second

Contrast this sequence, each picture showing a separate shot, with that of the 1878 revolver on the preceding pages. In 1 the bullet is just outside the barrel but still behind the vanguard of leaking gas; in 2 it has drawn ahead of its propelling charge and is entering the advanced leakage; and in 3 it is clearing all gas. Note the vortices in the gas.

By using the sight as a reference, stages of the return of the barrel from its recoil may be noted. The round object in the foreground is a microphone which starts the stroboscopic light when it picks up the sound of the discharge. The distance of the microphone from the gun governs the timing of the photograph since sound travels at a known velocity (about 1,100 feet per second)

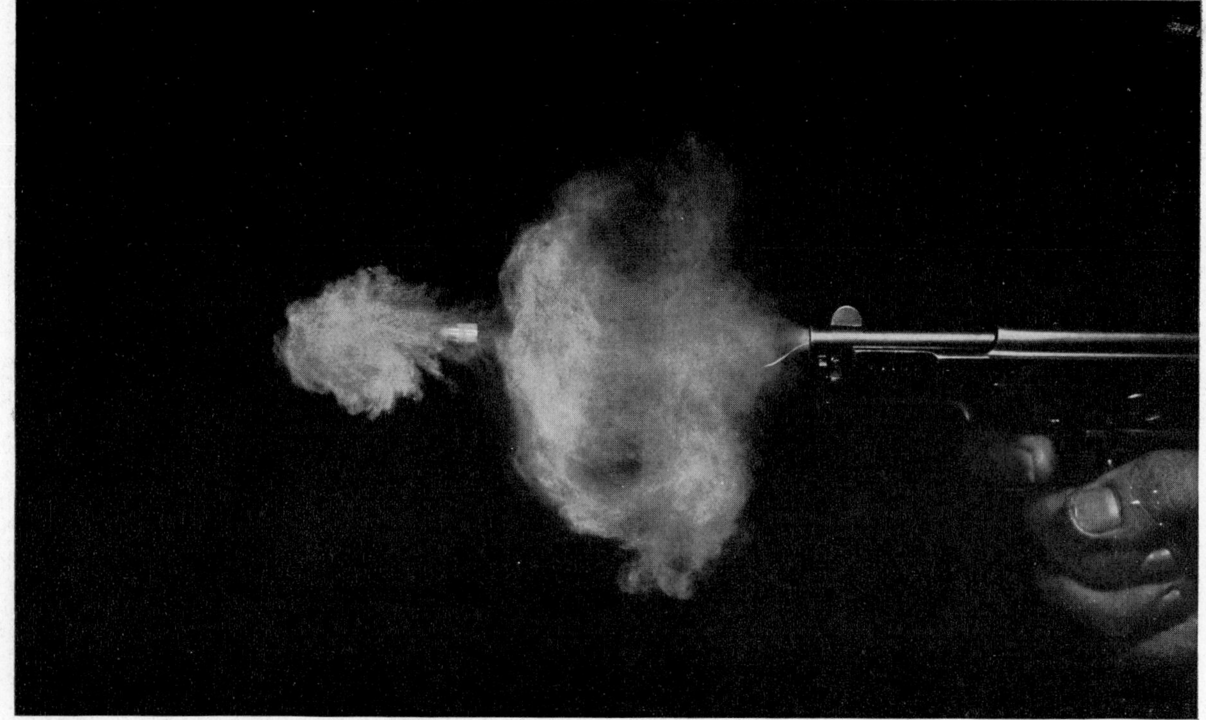

2

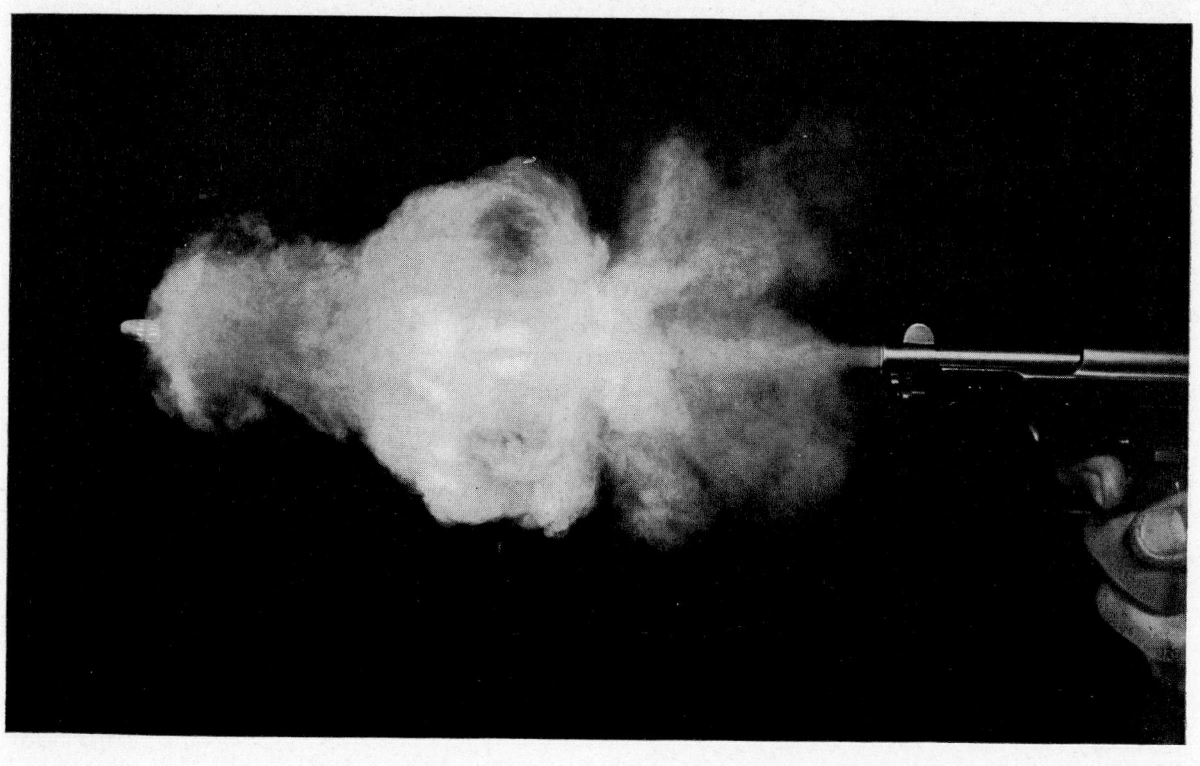

3

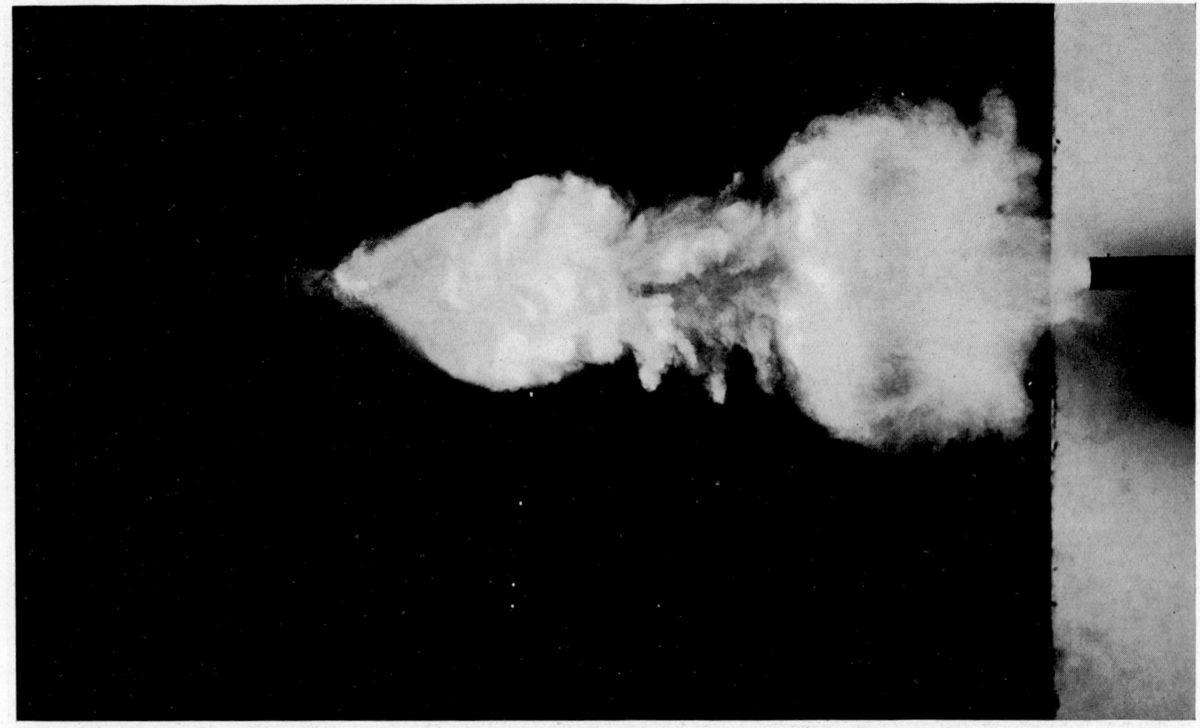

At the right may be seen the muzzle and out in front of the gas, the front wad

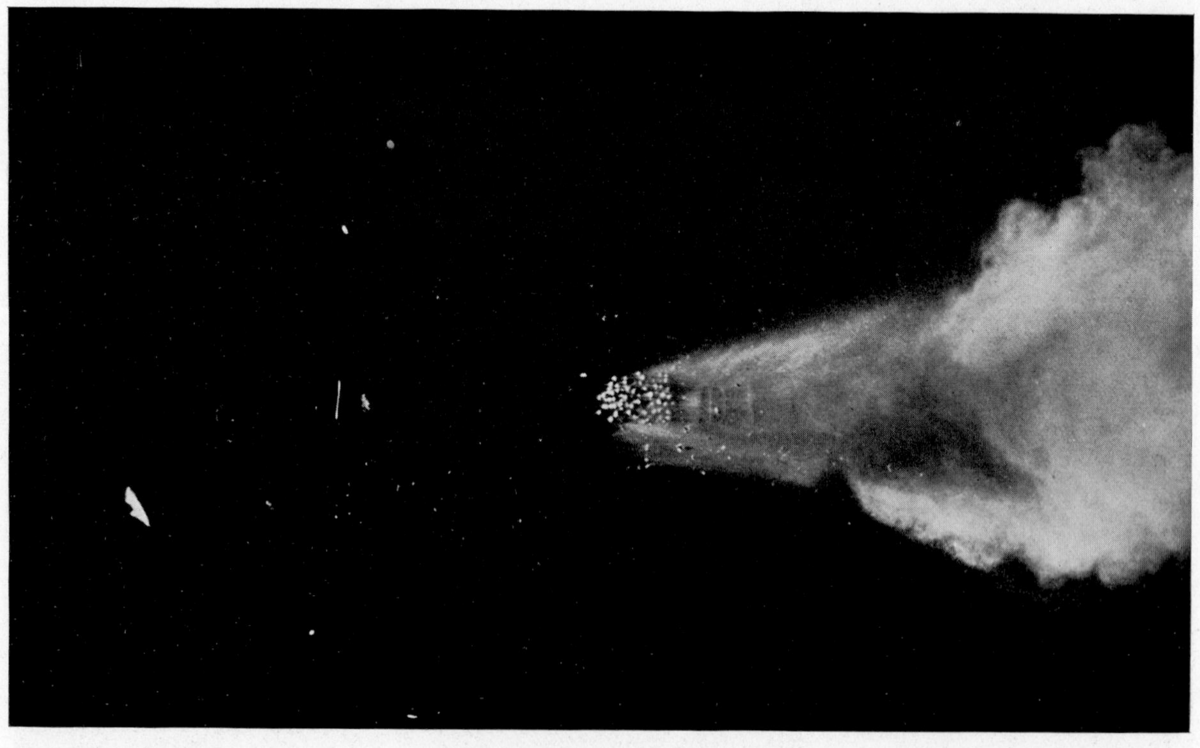

Here the shot pulls out of the gas

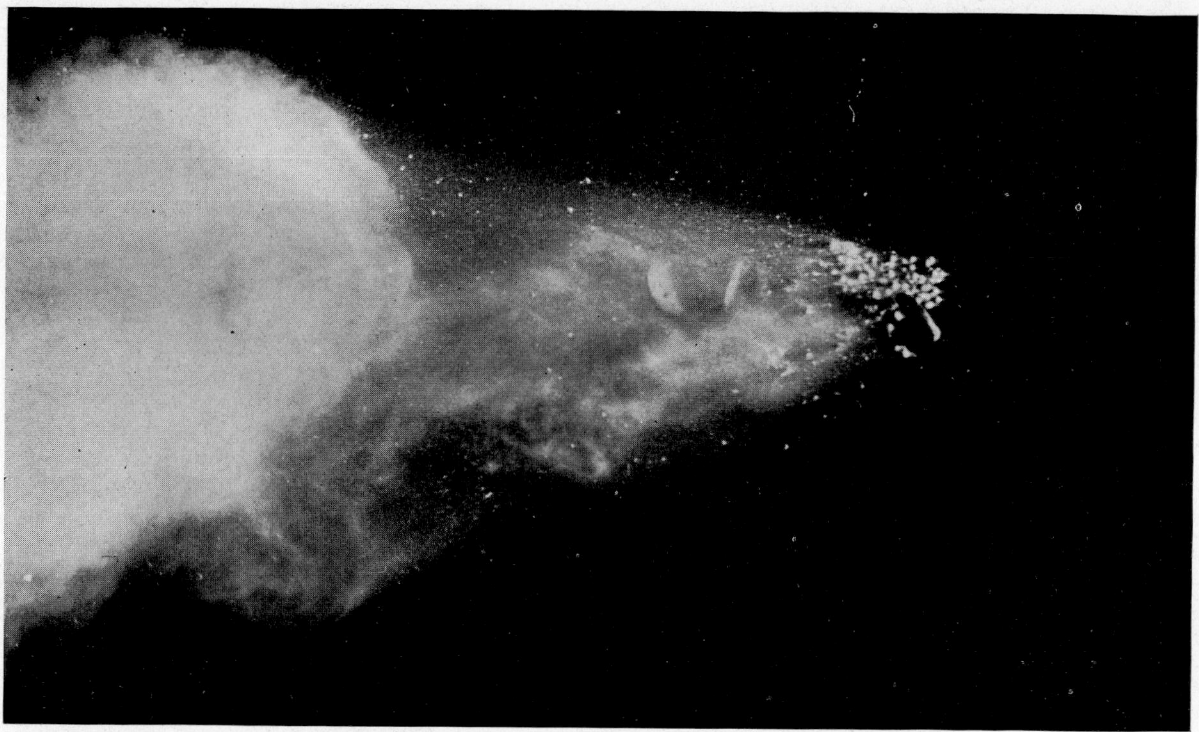

Behind the shot may be seen the tumbling wads

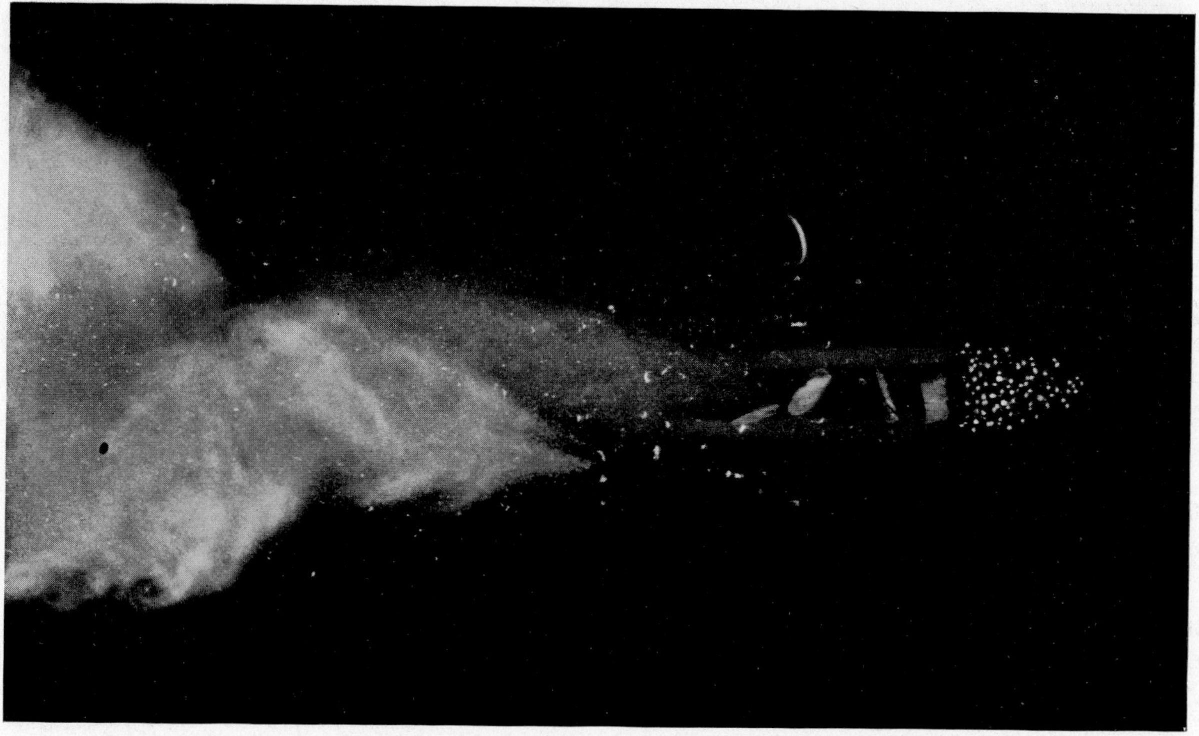

Note here the formation of the shot

COLLISION AT 1,800 MILES PER HOUR!

Cruising along at this speed a bullet encounters an electric-light bulb, and the high-speed camera reports the details of the accident.

1

The speed of this .30-caliber bullet is approximately 2,700 feet per second, or over 1,800 miles per hour, and the action shown in the four pictures lasts about 3/10,000ths of a second, each picture being exposed one-millionth of a second.

In 1 it is approaching the bulb, and at the base of the light is a double-exposure view of all that was left of bulb at the end; in 2 the rifling grooves and even the crimp

2

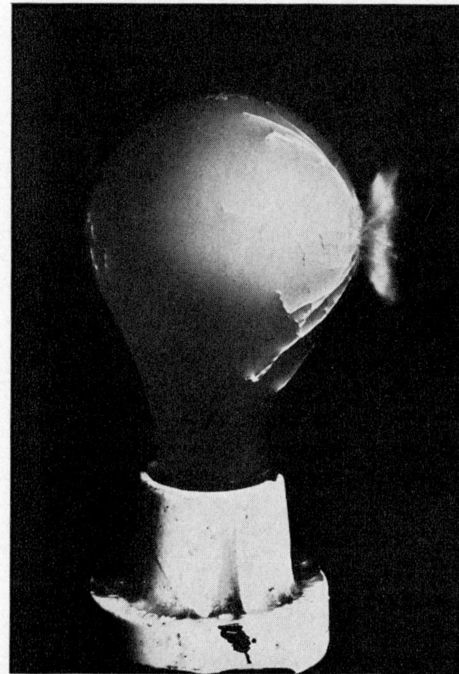

marks where the shell was attached are clearly visible as well as the cracks which are traveling faster than the bullet; in 3 it is just inside, and the compression wave (traveling about 15,000 feet per second) in the glass cracks the other side before the bullet gets there; and in 4 it is several inches beyond the bulb and emerging from the arrowhead formation of gas and glass dust that accompanied it out of the bulb. A split second later the bulb becomes a cascade of falling glass fragments.

3

The four pictures were not taken in succession; each is of a different bullet and a different bulb caught at different phases of the action.

4

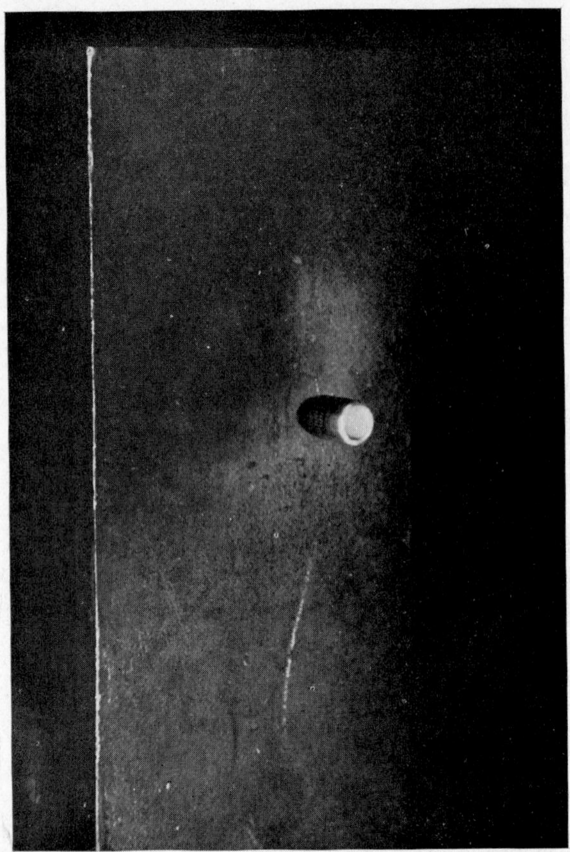

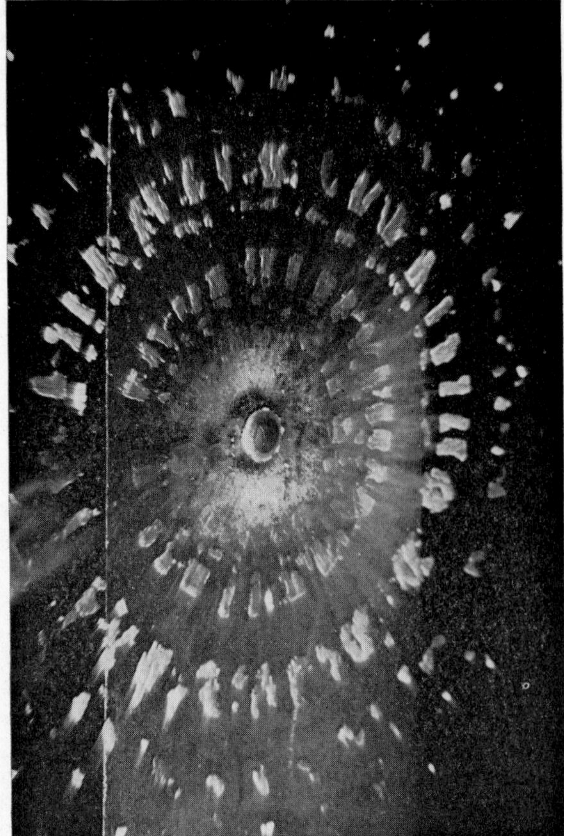

THIS HAS NEVER BEEN SEEN BEFORE

Exposure: 1/1,000,000 of a second When a .22 bullet strikes a steel block, it apparently liquefies from the force of the impact and splashes in a manner not unlike the milk drops shown on page 122. As the liquid lead splatters and solidifies again, the particles radiate outward in the charming concentric-circle formation seen in the adjacent picture. The origin of the concentric circles is probably the grooved marking of the bullet, visible in the first picture. Highlights in the pictures of the splatter show that the liquid lead has a peculiar surface like molten or polished silver.

Inspection of armor plate after being struck by high-powered projectiles shows permanent splash formations similar to those in liquids seen on page 122, thus showing that the metal momentarily acted as a liquid

SPORTS

By recording motion in relation to time, the motion picture has contributed to almost every sport in which speed and control are important. Its chief deficiency has been its slowness; the speed range of the most modern cameras designed for motion study is too restricted to provide a lucid record of many actions.

Ultrahigh-speed photography, both motion and still, has at last broken through this restriction and provided a means for studying form and technique equal to any speed within the capacity of performers. Examples of the application of high-speed still photography to golf, badminton, tennis, baseball, squash rackets, football, and other games are shown in the pages immediately following. Of the games so far studied golf has been most thoroughly analyzed, and an example of how the data supplied by the pictures are used for detailed scientific analyses is given on pages 61 to 63. Other sports involving impact and flight are amenable to the same thorough investigation, and already the high-speed method is aiding in developing better performance and in designing sporting equipment to respond more efficiently to the skill of the player.

It has been in the field of sports that the newest and most spectacular form of high-speed photography—multiple exposure—has been most extensively used, and many of the pictures, beginning on page 58, were made by this method.

WHEN THE BALL IS STRUCK

On this, the preceding, and the opposite page are four studies of what occurs when a golf club strikes a golf ball. In the last picture note the egg-shaped form assumed by the ball. For a period after its compression by the club the ball oscillates, swelling and shrinking along the horizontal axis

MULTIPLE 1/100,000 OF A SECOND EXPOSURES OF GOLF STROKES

Multiple-exposure photography, the newest extension of the high-speed technique, developed at the Massachusetts Institute of Technology, yields these extraordinary records of golf strokes. These composite photographs are obtained by taking superimposed pictures on the same plate at successive intervals of time, the intervals being controlled and known.

The above picture shows clearly the distortions, both bending and twisting, of the shaft during a stroke by Joe Stein. The time interval between exposures, that is, between the flashes of light producing the images, is 1/600 of a second. The club as it approaches the ball, can be seen to run slightly ahead of the shaft. Impact with the ball twists the shaft and produces a marked bend which straightens out later, the head then resuming its forward position.

Multiple-flash (300 per second) photograph of a driver, showing the distortion wave running up the shaft after the ball is hit. The stage of the stroke showing the s-bend in the shaft comes a little less than 1/1,000 of a second after contact. The image of the traveling ball between alternate images of the shaft shows that the ball is traveling twice as fast as the club head after impact

Single flash of Bobby Jones making an iron shot. The squashed ball indicates that the light flashed at the exact moment of impact

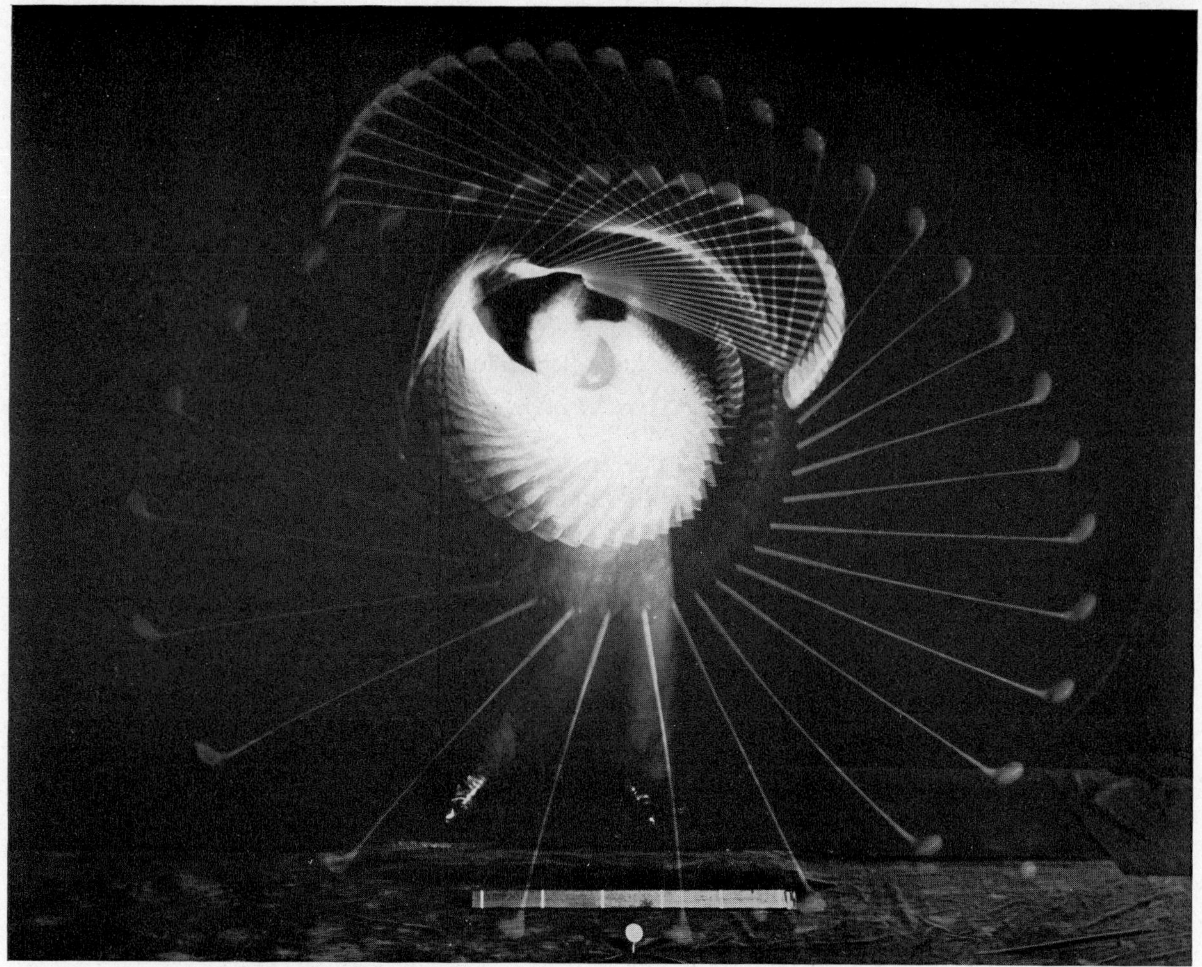

Multiple flash of Jones with a driver. Here the interval between exposures is 1/100 of a second, the exposure time 1/100,000 of a second. This photograph reveals that the ball velocity is 225 feet per second; the club velocity before impact, 166 feet per second; after impact, 114 feet per second

CATCHING THE CLICK

Is there a golfer who has not wondered what happens during the "click"—that all-important event when the club imparts its energy and the skill of the player to the ball? And how many inconclusive arguments have been waged in locker rooms over the questions:

1. Is the follow-through really important?
2. Does overspin of the ball rather than backspin ever occur in normal play?
3. Does the club impart the spin, or is the spin produced by the action of the air on the ball?
4. Does a heavy club produce a longer drive than a light one?

The pictures on the following pages, taken by the single-flash and multiflash technique, show clearly the details of the click.

When these photographs are analyzed, we see clearly that the club and ball are in contact for a brief time and that they travel together for only a very short distance. The time of contact is about half a thousandth of a second (0.0005 second), and the distance they travel together is less than an inch (about 0.8 inch). From a golfer's standpoint, the ball is off the club face when the face has advanced to a position over the center line of the tee. During this extremely short interval the ball is compressed (see page 57) and springs away from the club head. Thus the club imparts its momentum to the ball by impact, and there is no follow-through action whereby the club continues to push and direct the ball. It is impossible for the golfer to manipulate the ball while it is on the face of the club.

A black cross is painted on the ball in order to determine the spin. Measurement of the angular shift of these lines between flashes combined with the known time between flashes makes it possible to determine the speed of rotation. All normal shots show backspin. Measurements of spin give figures from about 2,000 revolutions per minute for balls hit with drivers up to about 10,000 r.p.m. for balls hit with more lofted clubs, such as a No. 7 iron. Since a ball is in the air for about six seconds, it turns over 200 times in traveling from tee to turf, assuming constant speed of rotation.

In two of the illustrations the velocities and accelerations have been plotted in polar co-ordinates and superimposed on the photographs of No. 2 irons swung by Bobby Jones and by an ordinary golfer. A great deal of information is summarized on these plots, in graphic form.

The velocity of Bobby Jones's stroke increases up to the moment of impact, while that of the ordinary golfer is falling off at impact. The maximum of acceleration occurs earlier for Bobby Jones than for the ordinary golfer. The timing of Bobby Jones is better: The ordinary golfer "quits too soon." The velocity curve for Bobby Jones is heart shaped except for the abrupt change at impact, a demonstration of the remarkable smoothness and symmetry of his downstroke and follow through.

When they see multiple-flash photographs of strokes, expert golfers are usually surprised to discover that the ball travels faster than the club. If the ball and club were perfectly elastic, the ball would travel nearly twice as fast as the club in accordance with the principle of the conservation of energy and momentum. Practical balls, however, are not perfectly elastic, and experimentally their velocity is found to be only about 40 per cent greater than that of the club. A heavy club (head weight 11.6 ounces, for example) gives an increase in speed over that of the club of about 47 per cent, while a light club (head weight about 7.2 ounces) gives a 36 per cent increase. The light club, however, is usually swung enough faster to make up for the difference.

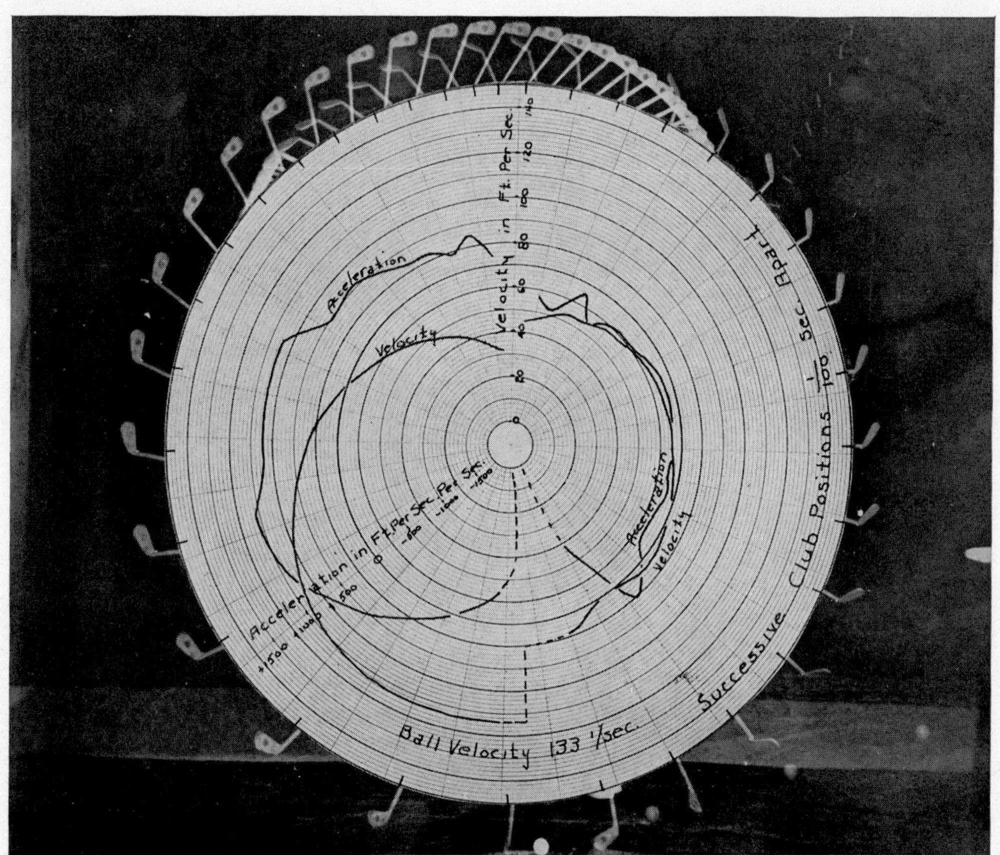

UNSKILLED

Graphical analysis of an unskilled golfer's stroke

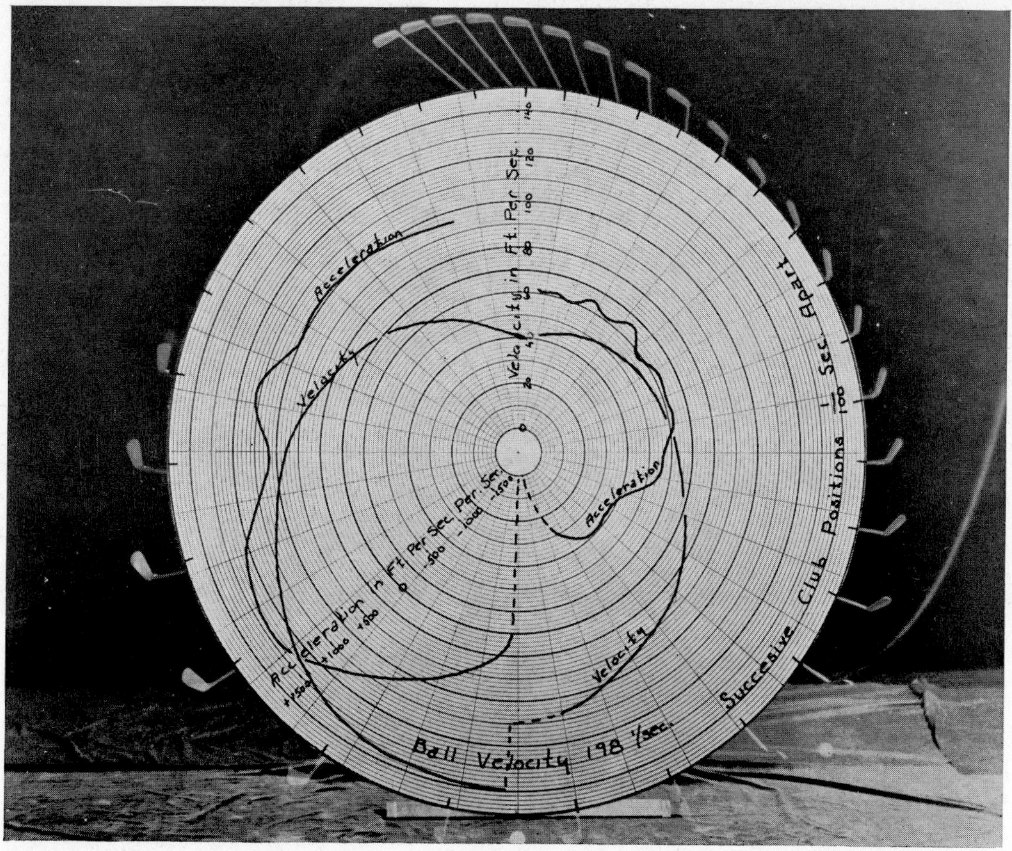

SKILLED

Here is Bobby Jones's record. For an explanation of these graphs see opposite page. For the picture from which this was made see page 65.

Side-view multiple flash of Bobby Jones. Here is clearly seen the plane of the swing

Jones with an iron. Note the arc of his swing, the varying speed of the club around the arc (speed may be determined by the distance between pictures of the club). Two images of the ball in flight were caught, and the distance between them yields the velocity of the ball since the time interval (1/100 of a second) between exposures is known. In this picture the ball velocity is 198 feet per second; the club velocity before impact, 136 feet per second; after impact, 102 feet per second. The divisions on the scale are six inches apart.
The second image of the ball is lost against the scale

Here is an ordinary golfer. It's a toe shot, and the twist of the club head is readily seen. Note the trace of the tee as it flies upward.

Compare this stroke with those of Jones, Guldahl, Shute, Thomson, and other top-flight golfers on the preceding and following pages. This picture furnished the data for the first graph on page 63

A skilled woman golfer executed this symmetrical oval stroke. Golf experts say she turned her hands too soon. Result: smothering. The ghostlike quality of the players in these multiple-flash pictures is the result of dozens of separate exposures superimposed

Rhythm, speed, concentration, and control are all apparent in this single-flash study of Mr. Shute driving. The intent expression on his face was too fleeting for any ordinary candid camera. Note the photoelectric cell used for timing flash. Approximately 1/1,000 of a second has elapsed since impact

DENSMORE SHUTE

Golfers had best interpret this swing analysis for themselves, but the laymen will notice the bend in the shaft after the ball is struck. Interval of time between pictures: 1/100 of a second

RALPH GULDAHL

The flying necktie, no less than the flying ball and the dynamic swing of his body, shows the movement of Mr. Guldahl's stroke at contact position. Here again may be seen the ultracandid candor of the high-speed camera. A microphone, rather than a photoelectric cell, was used to time the picture. Sound travels so slowly that the ball is well on its way when the light is finally actuated by the sound of impact. Place a straight edge along the shaft to see the distortion clearly.

Lay a straight edge along any one of the pictures of the club's shaft if you want to study the bending of the club. Mr. Guldahl's stroke is a good one to analyze

ROLAND WINGATE

Observe Mr. Wingate's position and the bend in the shaft with the head still in front despite its contact with the ball

Mr. Wingate can drive a ball through a telephone book. For the benefit of skeptics he did it before the high-speed camera.

JAMES THOMSON; HOW HE DRIVES

The form which Thomson uses in making his famous long drives is shown in the above multiple-exposure analysis and in the eight single-flash photographs on the next four pages. In the photograph above, which is a superimposed picture of the stroke shown in the last six pictures of the following series, the marked bending of the club may be seen as well as the way Thomson wraps the club around his neck at the beginning and end of the stroke.

And now start at the top of the next page for a step-by-step analysis of Thomson's drive

ADDRESS TO THE BALL

ON THE UPSWING

START OF SWING. NOTE HOW HE KEEPS HIS EYES ON THE BALL

HE BEGINS TO PUT SNAP INTO THE CLUB

CENTRIFUGAL FORCE ACTING ON THE HEAD TENDS TO BEND THE SHAFT

BY CAREFUL TIMING THE CAMERA CATCHES THE POINT OF CONTACT

ON THE FOLLOW-THROUGH

AT THE WINDUP THE EYES BEGIN TO FOLLOW BALL

HORTON SMITH DRIVING

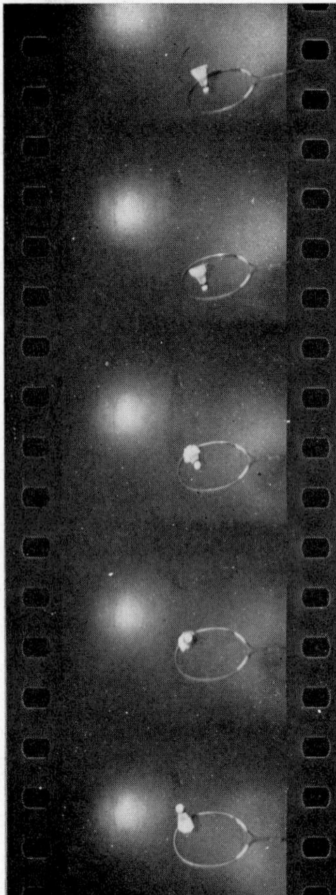

THE BIRD TURNS

When the bird is hit by the racket in badminton, it executes an unexpected about turn instead of rebounding straightaway, and it makes its complete turn in less than 1/100 of a second. In the adjacent illustrations No. 1 is a moving-picture sequence in which the bird is hit between the first and second frames. Nos. 2-6 are single exposures, each of a separate stroke, that tell the same story in greater detail. The strokes were executed by Jack Brewer, the well-known badminton coach and professional

1. Enlargement of a section of high-speed film taken at 560 frames a second, showing five successive phases of the bird's complete turn after being struck

2. Just before impact the feathers are unruffled. The exposure here is 1/100,000th of a second as it is in the four succeeding pictures

3. The moment of impact, the racket strings bending upward, and the bird with its feathers ruffled beginning to turn over

4. The bird takes off and starts to turn tail with its feathers badly ruffled. The racket's rim is bent and strings are taut again

5. The bird completes its turn and starts on its trajectory, its feathers smooth again. The racket follows but at a slower speed

6. As in the preceding picture the handle of the racket here is still bent as the stroke continues and the bird sails away

TENNIS

In the pictures of prominent tennis players on the following pages is found further evidence of the analytical power of single-flash and multiple-exposure photography. Both techniques are being used for the study of sports equipment, both may be used to investigate the principles of impact and flight as they affect performance. In the single-flash picture above is seen the squash of a tennis ball and the indenting of the strings as the ball is hit

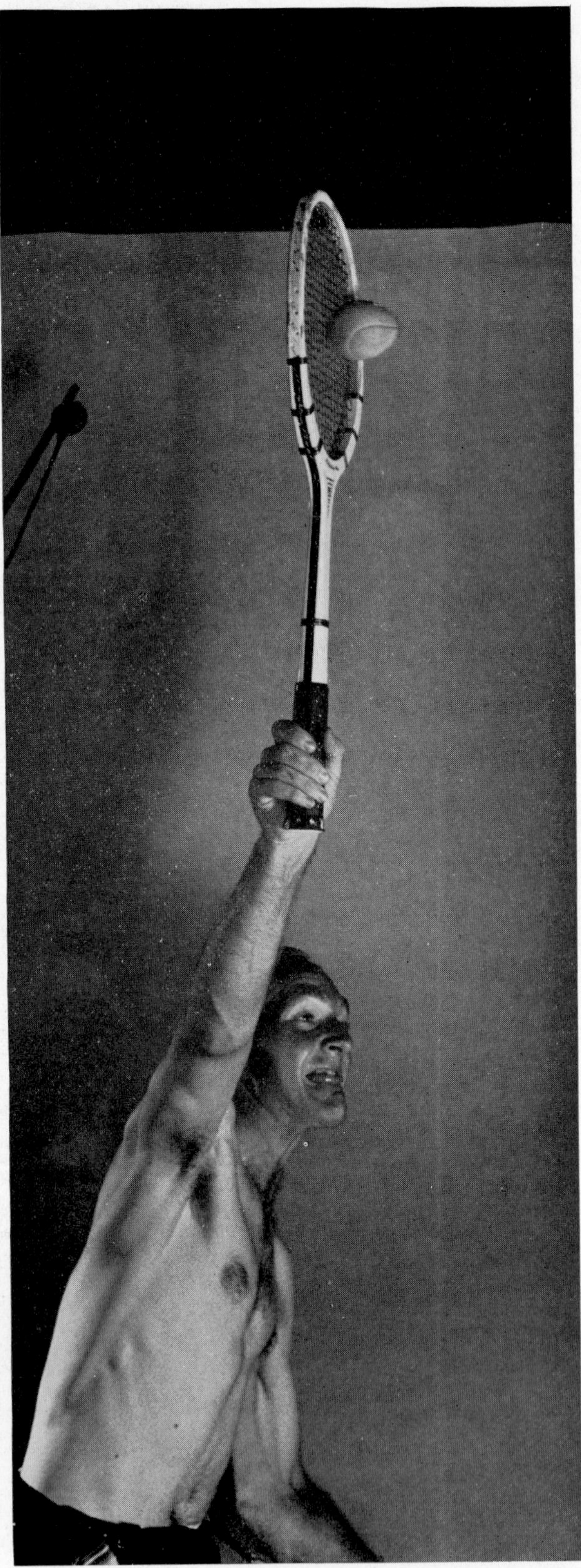

JOHN BROMWICH

Most striking features in these three studies are the effects of impact on the shape of the ball (ranging from a flattening on both sides to a pulsating egg shape) and the apparently inevitable appearance of Mr. Bromwich's tongue at the moment of impact. Pronounced bending in the racket is observable in both pictures on the left

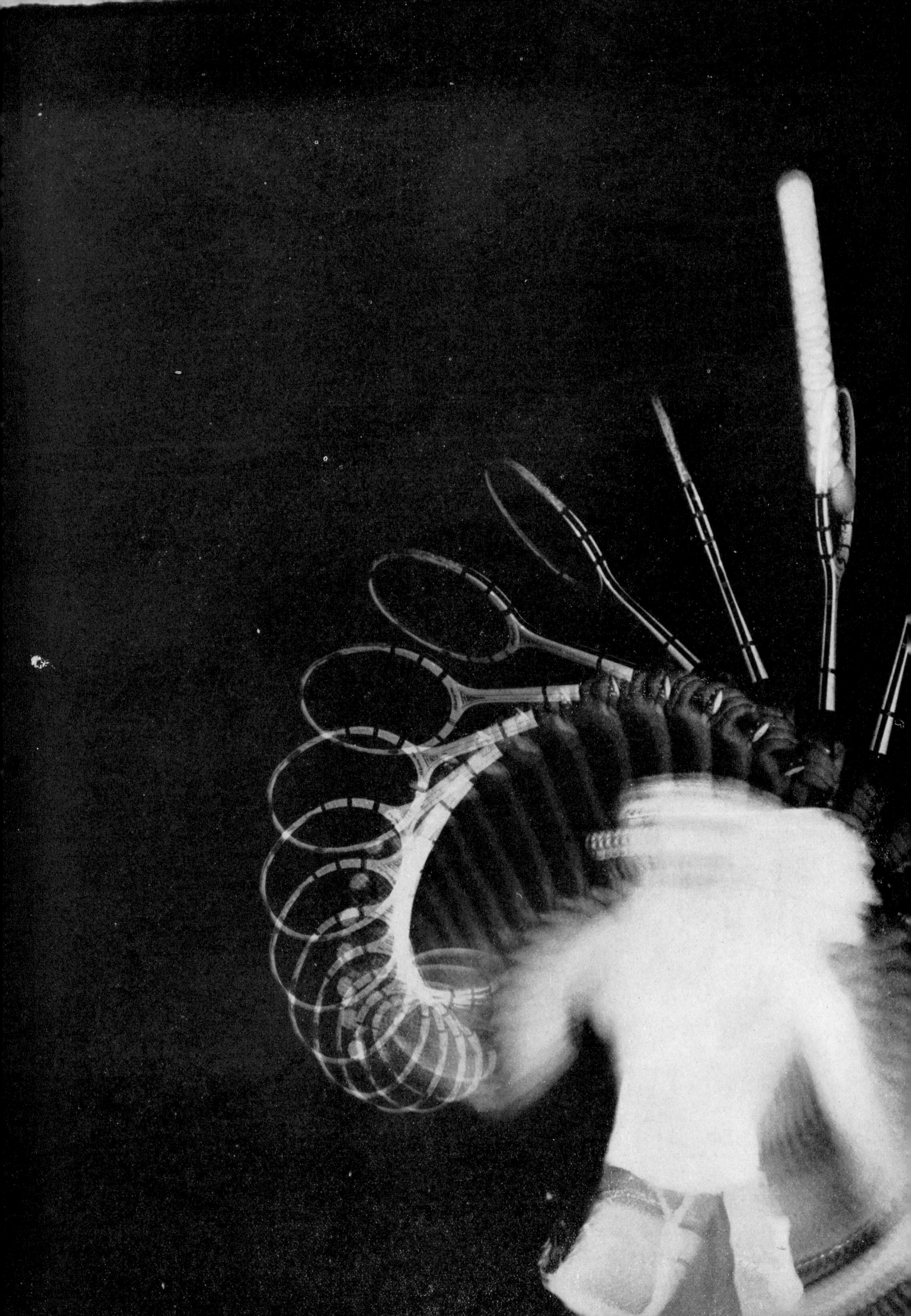

BROMWICH SERVES

Here the flashes were so timed in relation to the ball and racket that the moment of impact was caught exactly. Note that the ball is flattened on both back and front sides. Analysis shows that the tip of the racket vibrates back and forth after the impact

CHARLES HARE
The left-handed English player in three studies. The ball is low in the strokes shown opposite

300 PICTURES A SECOND

Multiple-exposure close-up of impact in a serve. The light missed a flash just before impact. The distortion of the racket, backward and forward, is clearly seen

THE SWIRLS AND EDDIES OF A STROKE

Multiple photography, by coalescing successive images, captures the entire flowing record of an action. Note the trailing blur of the player's profile

Yvon Petra keeps his eyes on where he wants the ball to go

Virginia Wolfenden serves

ROBERT L. RIGGS, JR., IN ACTION Gjon Mili

BOBBY RIGGS; A HIGH-SPEED PORTRAIT Gjon Mili

SQUASH

John L. (Jack) Summers, many times champion, now coach at the

Massachusetts Institute of Technology, illustrates four strokes before the high-speed camera

TABLE TENNIS
Leslie Lowry, 1938 New England champion

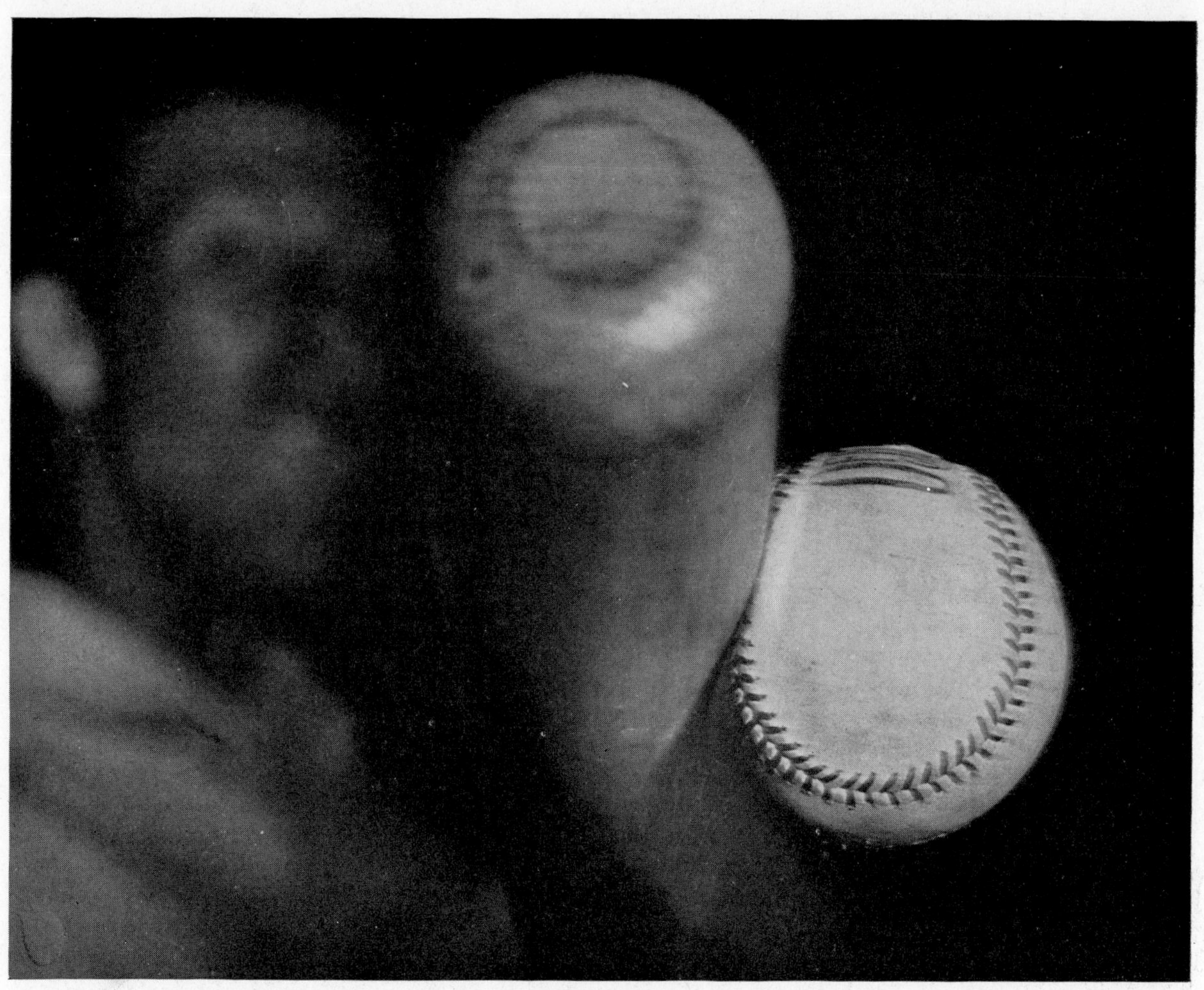

BASEBALL
Bat hits ball and ball shows it

The bat bends under the impact. The hit is low. Pictures like this can be helpful in studying form

Alphonse Lopez of the Boston Bees closes his eyes as he catches

CURVE-BALL PITCHING

Daniel MacFayden, great curve-ball pitcher of the Boston Bees, subjects himself to the analytical eye of the stroboscope.

Students of futuristic painting have lately pondered such composite pictures as the lower left one above, opined that such photographic records prove the validity of some misunderstood modern techniques

MACFAYDEN'S HAND IN ACTION

A clear record of how the ball is held, how it leaves the hand, how it is moving and at what speed. Note how the skin wrinkles and piles up on the back of his hand

PLACEMENT KICKS

Every football fan has seen a placement kick, but no one has observed what actually happens in that fraction of a second when the booter's toe meets the pigskin. In the picture above, note how the toe of the shoe is pushed backward. On the opposite page the kicker is Wesley E. Fesler, onetime all-American star at Ohio State, and the ball is inflated to the normal playing pressure of approximately 13 pounds to the square inch. Measurements show that the boot penetrates at least half the diameter of the ball. At the top of the ball, note the dust suspended in mid-air as the rapidly accelerated ball leaves. After leaving the foot, the ball pulsates, swelling and contracting as it recovers its usual contour

FENCING: MAKING THE FOIL BLADE FLY

Joseph Levis, five times national foils champion, executes this trick of the fencer. The blade is pressed against the floor, is released, flies upward, is caught

A SIMPLE SALUTE

Levis here executes the salute that a fencer gives before he engages his opponent

THE FLECHE

While practicing with an M.I.T. student, Levis (right) makes a surprise attack on the run.

In the fast fighting shown on the top of the next page, the student attacks Levis to his low line and Levis parries with a septieme. The student recovers to his right side, and Levis counterattacks into student's six line (his left line), hitting high near the student's collar.

Note the interesting movement of Levis' left hand behind his head. This hand helps to maintain balance during parries.

In the lower picture on the opposite page the student attacks to Levis' low line and Levis executes a low-line parry. He next makes a riposte to the student's chest. The left-handed student has gone back to cover his high line but finds no steel there

ARCHERY

In the picture above, the arrow has been in flight 1/30 of a second, the eyes of the archer are closed, the string painfully rolls up the skin on his unprotected arm.

In the pictures on the next page the arrow is bent first in one direction and then in the opposite direction as it whips around the bow

Above. Here is a good illustration of the "archer's paradox," the distortion of the arrow as it flexes about the bow.

Below. Exposures here were taken at the rate of 100 a second

LACROSSE

In the trajectory where the images of the ball are closely spaced, the ball is coming in toward the player. He catches it by a twisting movement of the stick, and by a swinging action returns it

LACROSSE, CONT.

The player tries to catch the incoming ball, but it strikes the edge of his stick instead of going into the basket. It then falls to the ground and bounces

This appears to be Janus himself, but it is only a multiple exposure of Henry P. McCarthy, physical training director, executing an Indian club routine.

Another routine is shown in the pictures on the next two pages. The first of these photographs is a result that can be obtained with a regular camera and is similar to the technique of recording abstract light patterns with which Ladislaus Molholy-Nagy of the Bauhaus experimented. The second of these pictures shows the same routine recorded by stroboscopic light

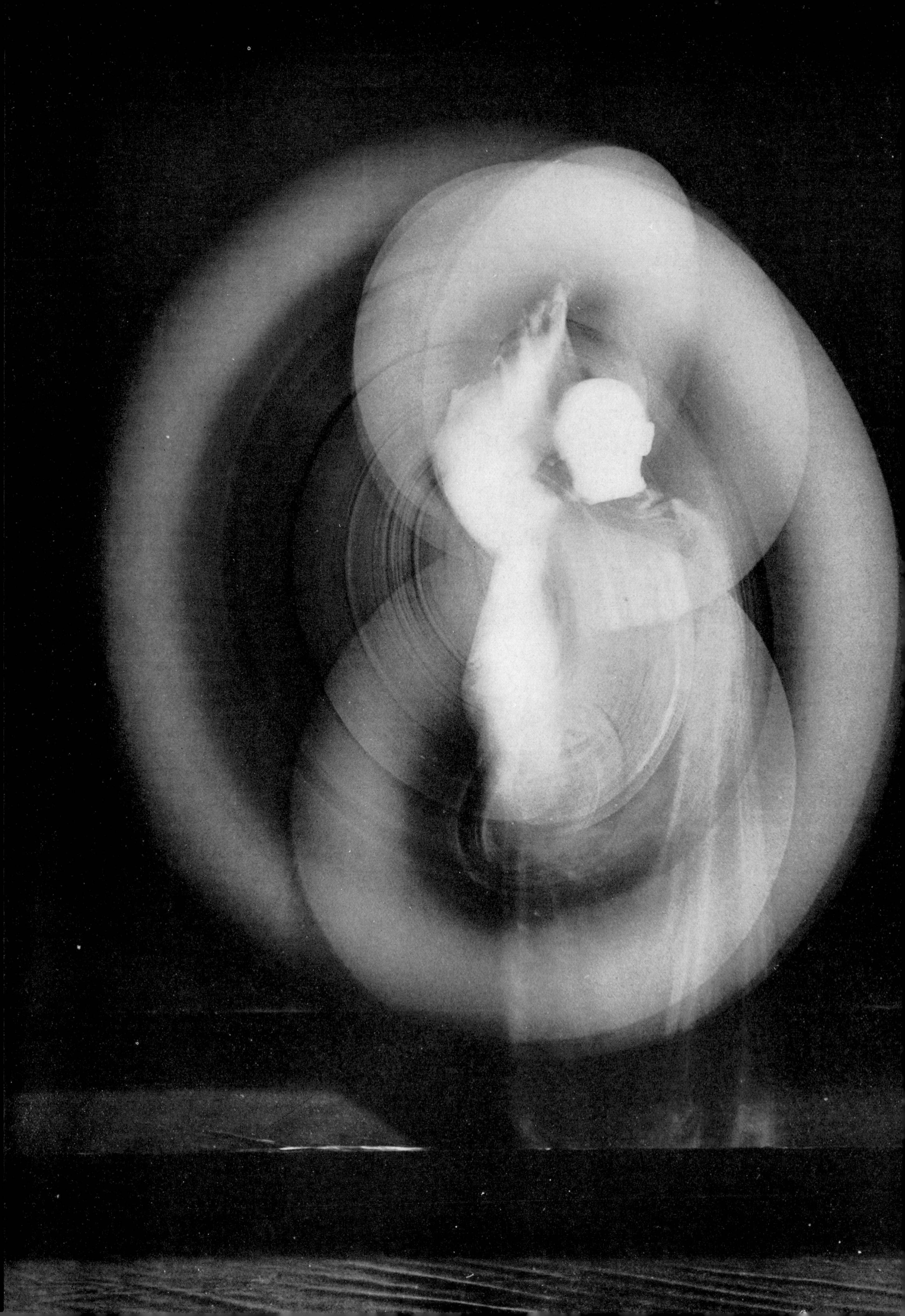

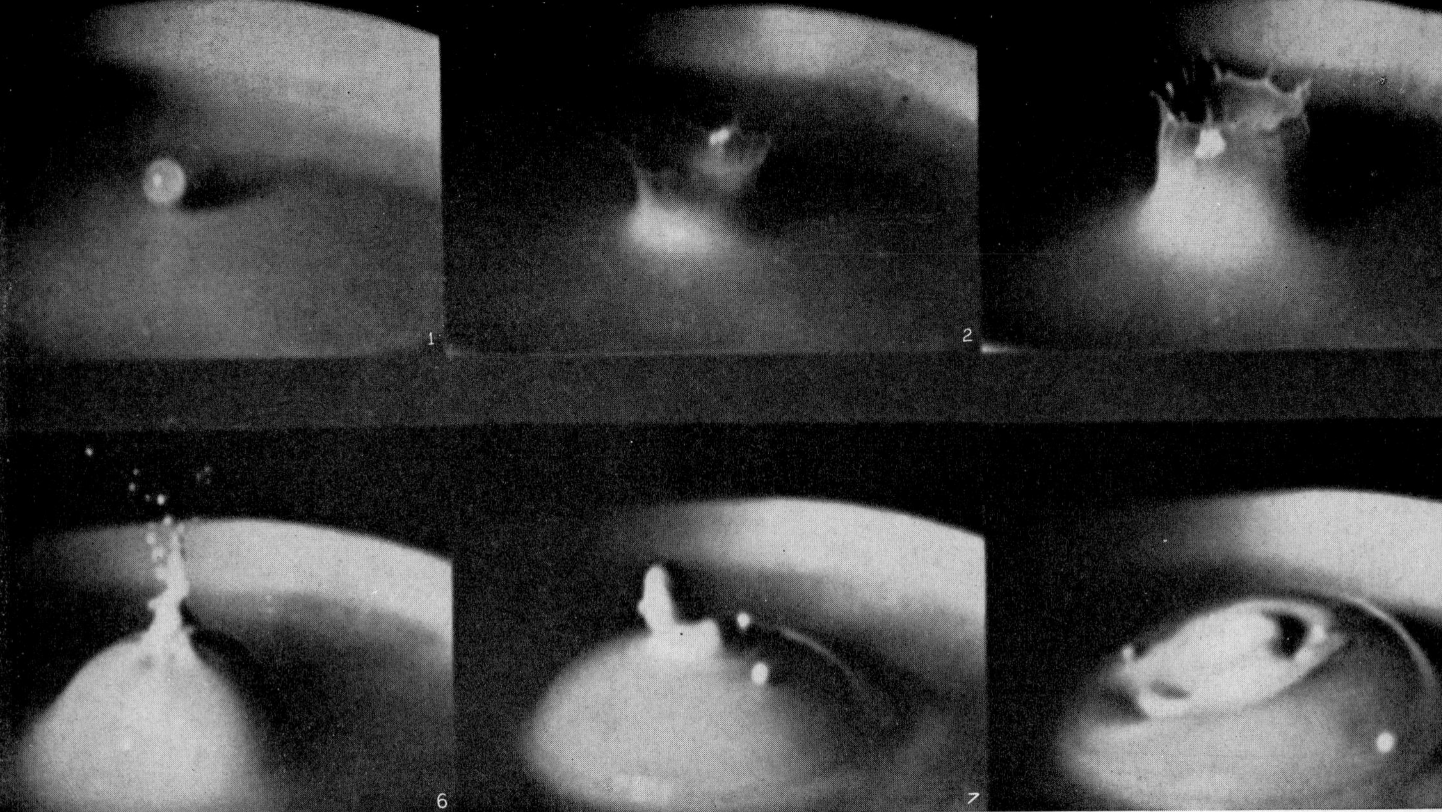

BIRTH OF A BUBBLE
A Drama of Surface Tension in Ten Scenes
When raindrops splash into a pool of water, they frequently form large bubbles that float on the surface for a brief span. Here this familiar phenomenon—the parturition of a bubble—is captured in detail in a sequence of ten pictures. Instead of water, milk is used because the photographic emulsion shows it more clearly

DROPS AND SPLASHES

In 1908, A. M. Worthington, professor of physics at the Royal Naval Engineering College, Devonport, England, published "A Study of Splashes." From his 14-year investigation, he wished "to share . . . some of the delight that I have myself felt, in contemplating the exquisite forms that the camera has revealed, and in watching the progress of a multitude of events, compressed within the limits of a few hundredths of a second, but none the less orderly and inevitable. . . ." Professor Worthington's photographs were the more remarkable for having been made in darkness with an electric spark, and he obtained many valuable experimental facts about surface tension and the changes of form that take place in the bounding surface of a liquid.

The pictures on the following pages represent a continuation of this pioneer investigation. "It would be an immense convenience," said he in his conclusion, "if we could use a kinematograph and watch such a splash in broad daylight, without the troublesome necessity of providing darkness and an electric spark. But the difficulties of contriving an exposure of the whole lens short enough to prevent blurring, either from the motion of the object, or from that of the rapidly shifting sensitive film, are very great, and anyone who may

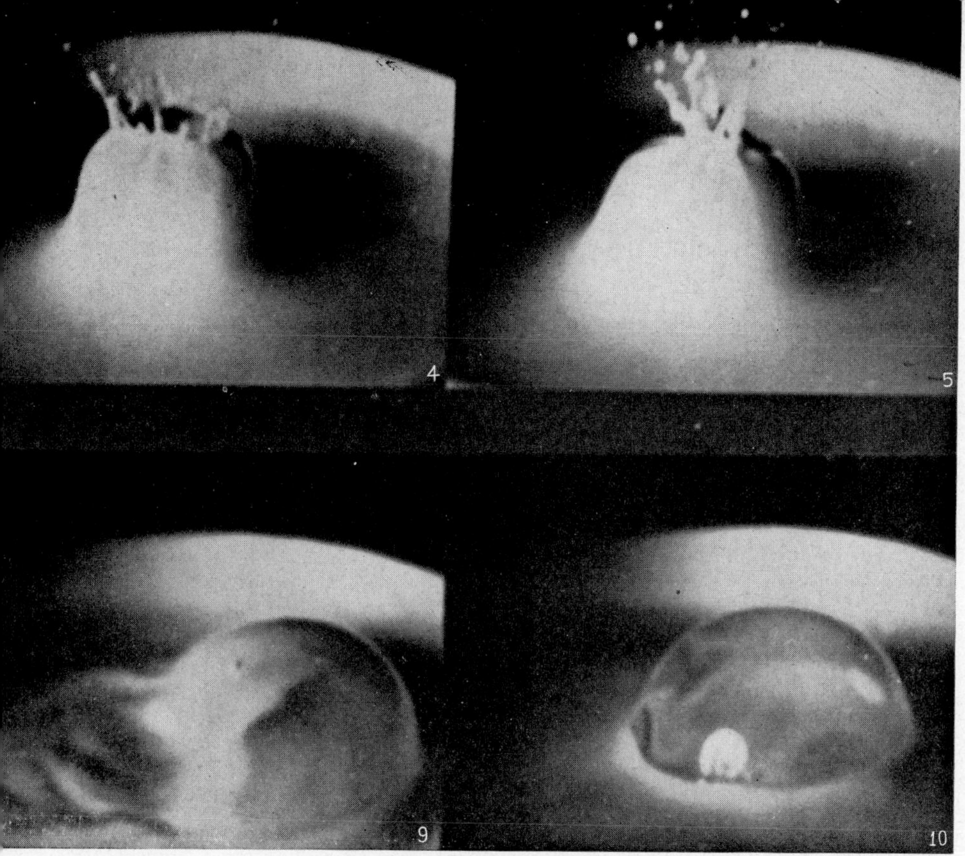

In picture 1 the drop is plummeting downward toward the surface of the pool of milk. Picture 2 catches the delicate crownlike formation of the splash, and pictures 3, 4, and 5 show the forces of surface tension, like the strings of a tobacco bag, acting to close the crown at the top and to entrap air within. In picture 6 comes the climax as the bubble, with an eruption of droplets, closes tight; in 7, 8, and 9 may be seen its contortions as it overcomes, by a narrow margin, the disruptive forces set up by the splash, and, finally, in 10 the shimmering bubble stands full-bodied and complete

be able to overcome them satisfactorily, will find a multitude of applications awaiting his invention." The modern stroboscope has achieved these desiderata, and under its revealing light it is now possible to see the exquisite splash formations with the unaided eye, to photograph them in daylight, and to take motion pictures for ultraslow projection.

In looking at the pictures of splashes and drops, two important principles should be kept in mind. First, the behavior of liquids is affected by surface tension. The surface layers of any liquid act like a stretched skin or membrane (a drumhead, for example) which is always trying to contract and diminish its area. Second, a spout or column of liquid, beyond a certain length in relation to its diameter, is unstable and tends to break down into a series of equidistant drops. As these drops are formed, they are joined together by narrow necks of liquid which in turn break up into smaller drops. A striking illustration may be seen in an ocean wave. At first the wave may have a smooth cylindrical edge. Then as the crest curls over, the edge becomes comblike, each tooth a jet which quickly breaks up into drops. The "principle of segmentation," be it noted, was first formulated by the blind physicist Plateau, who constructed the first stroboscope.

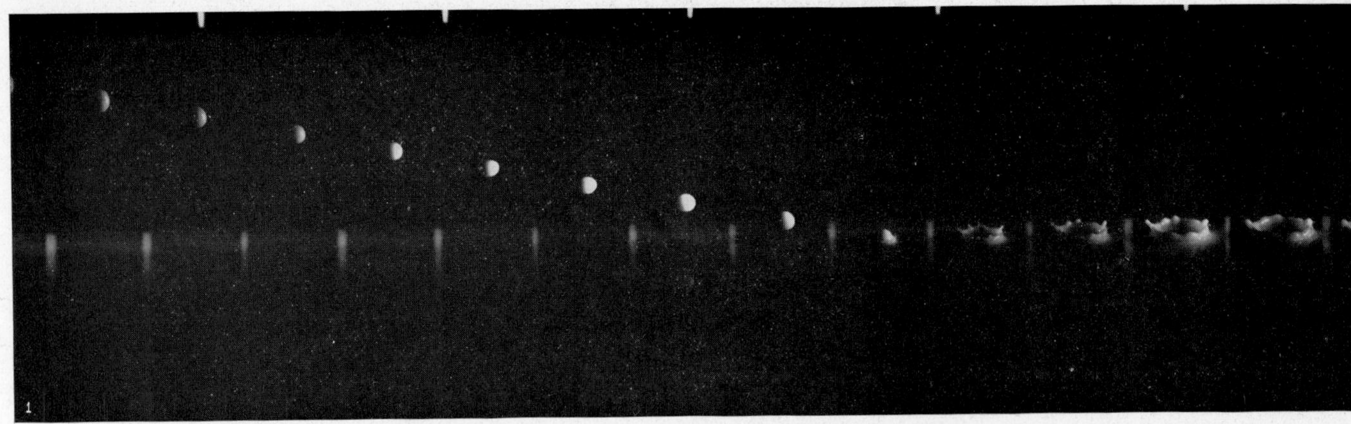

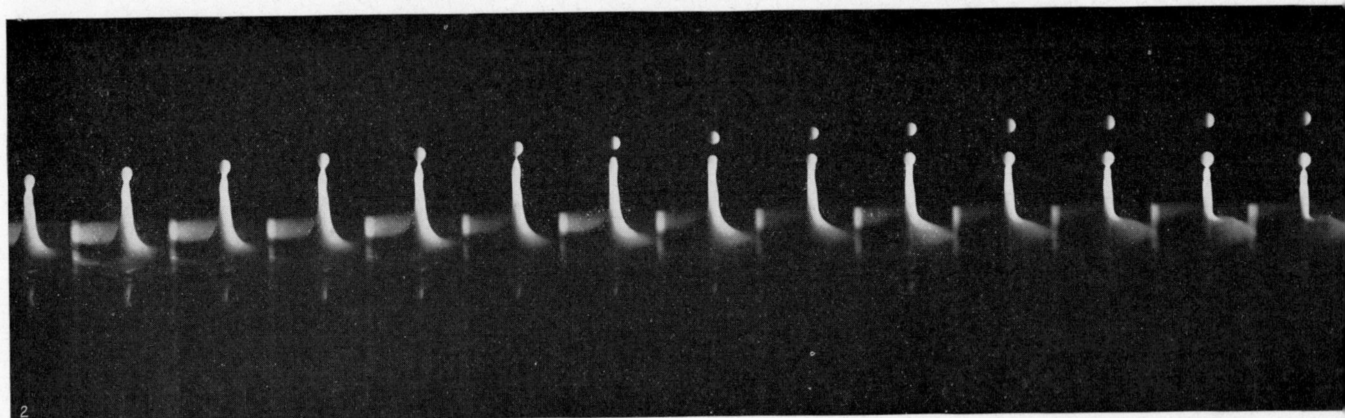

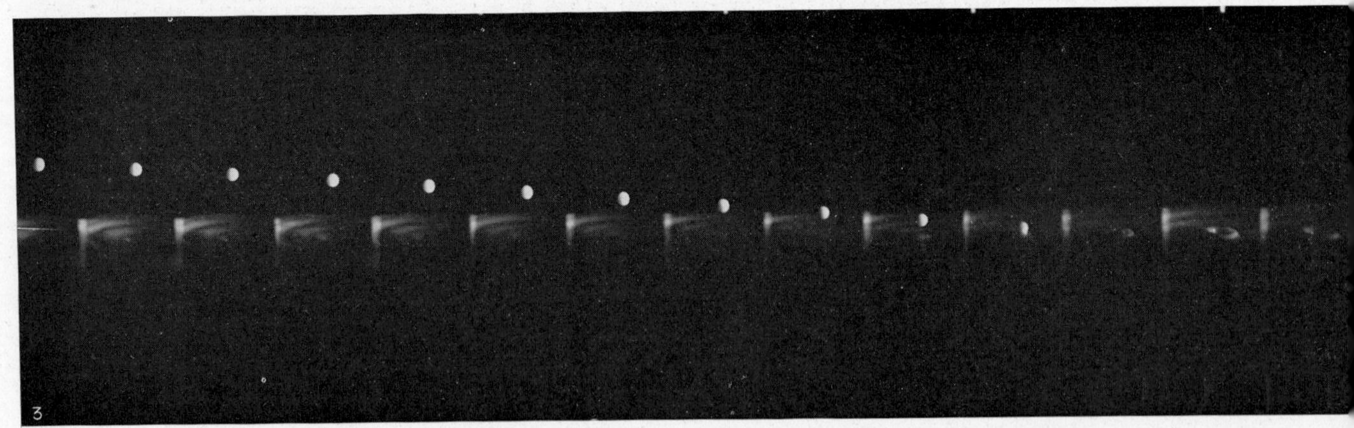

A FALLING DROP OF MILK CAUGHT IN THE ACT

Above is shown, from left to right across both pages, 90 separate, successive pictures of a globule of milk dropping into a puddle of milk.

When the drop strikes, as in the tenth picture, a crater is formed.

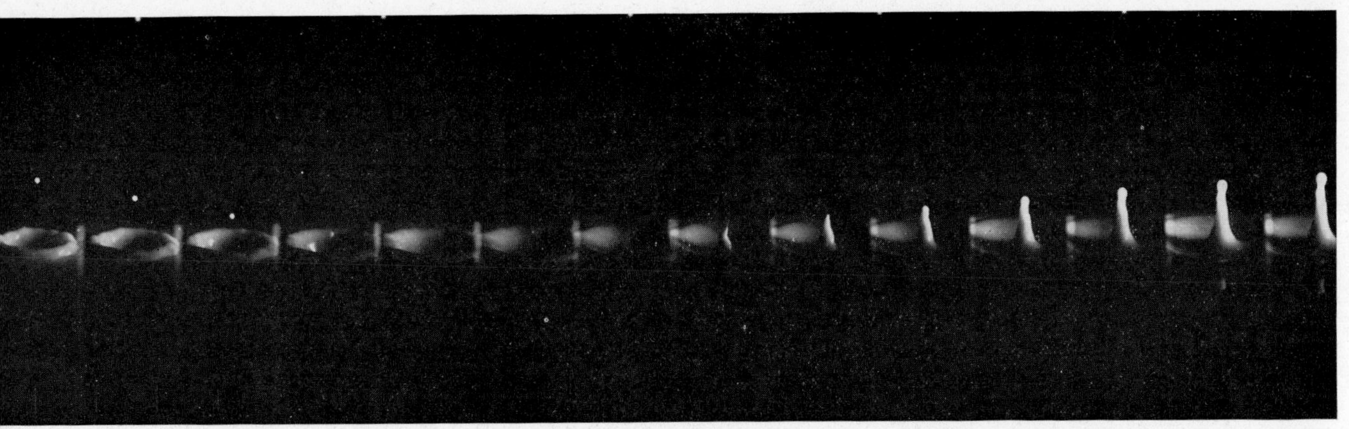

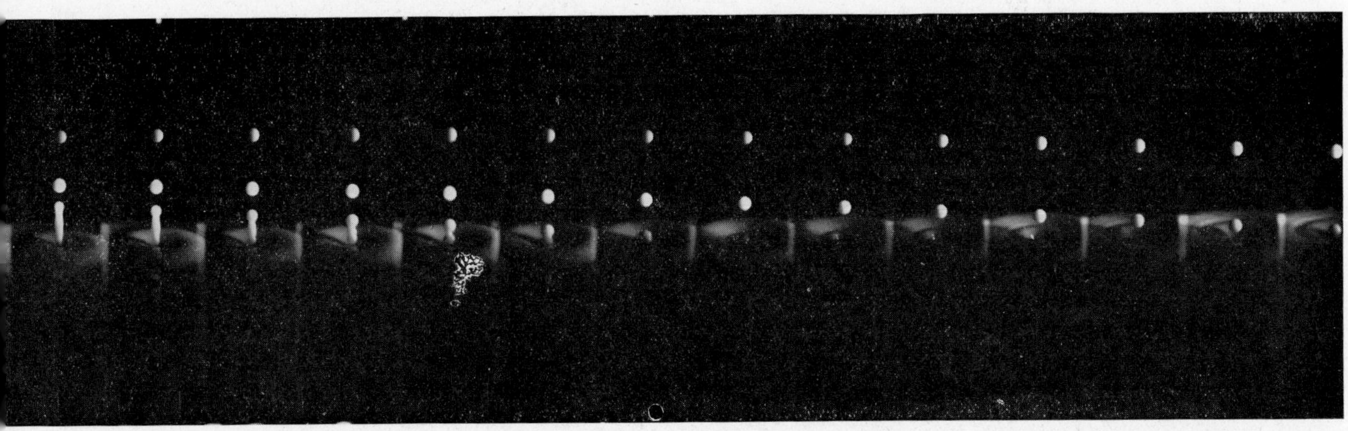

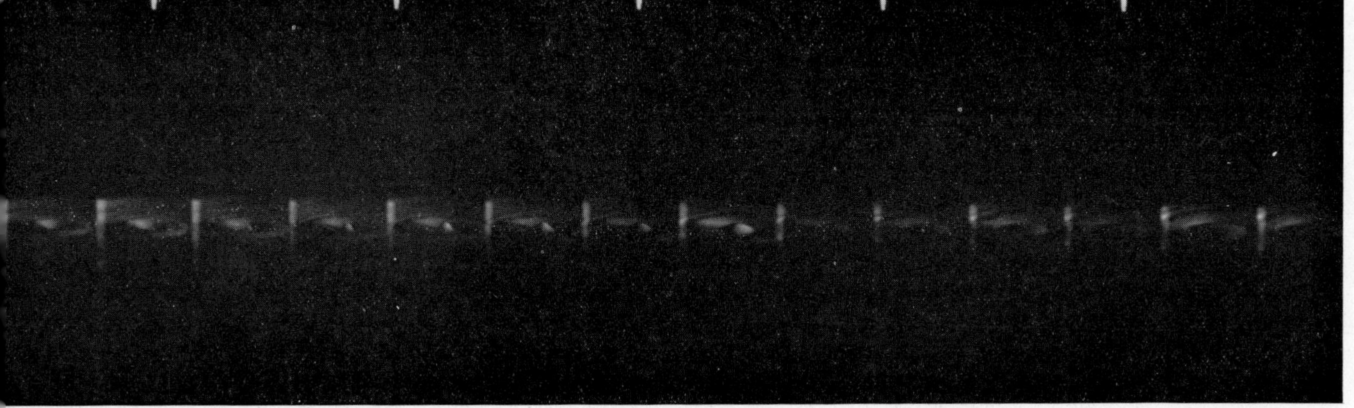

There next occurs a conical growth in the center of the crater, which resolves into small droplets after it spouts high. These droplets return to the crater, which pulsates itself ultimately out of existence.
Here in continuous sequence is the life history of a falling drop.
For individual chapters and incidents, see the next page

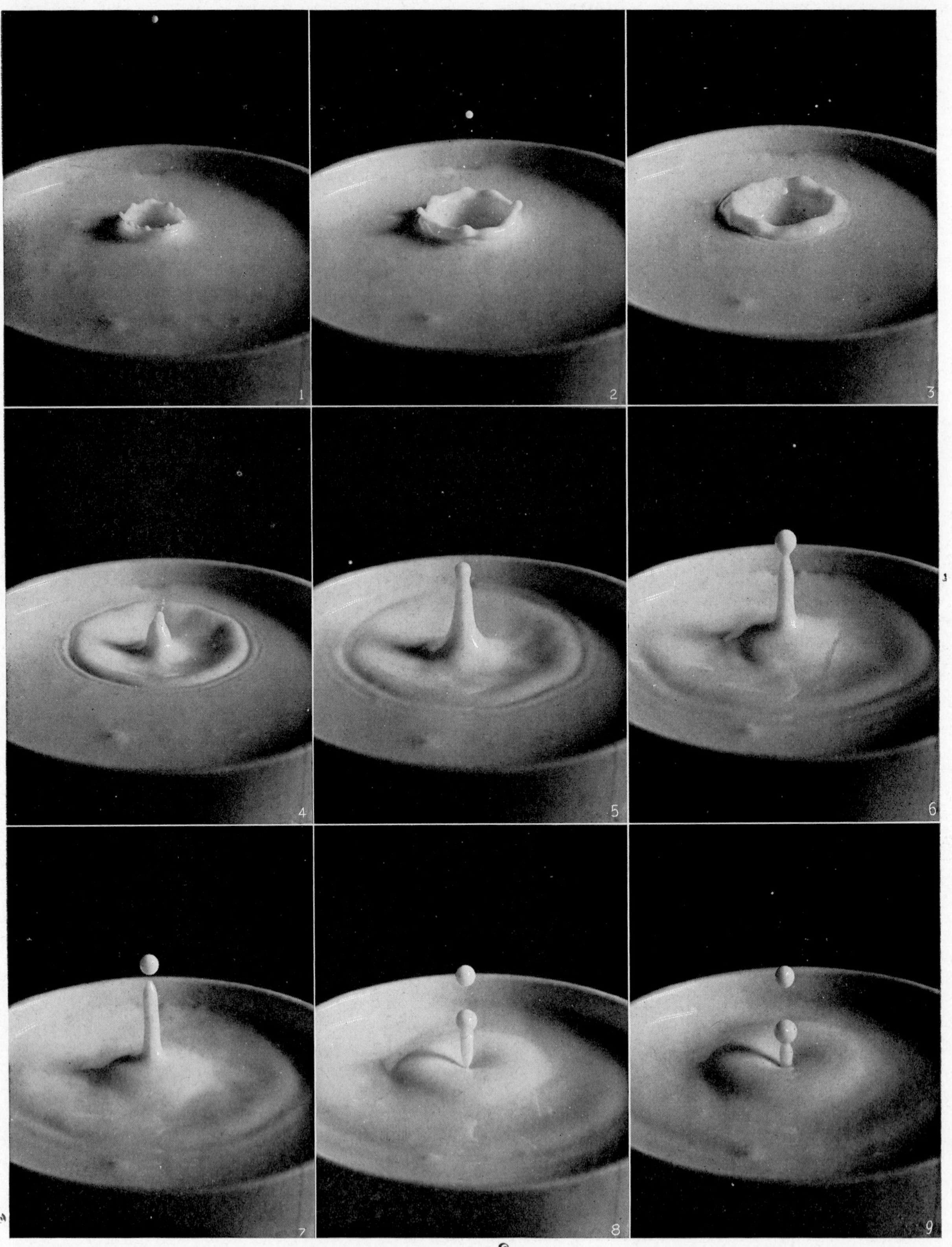

DROP FALLING INTO RESERVOIR OF MILK
Showing the formation and segmentation of the spout

Close-up of spout, showing drop breaking off

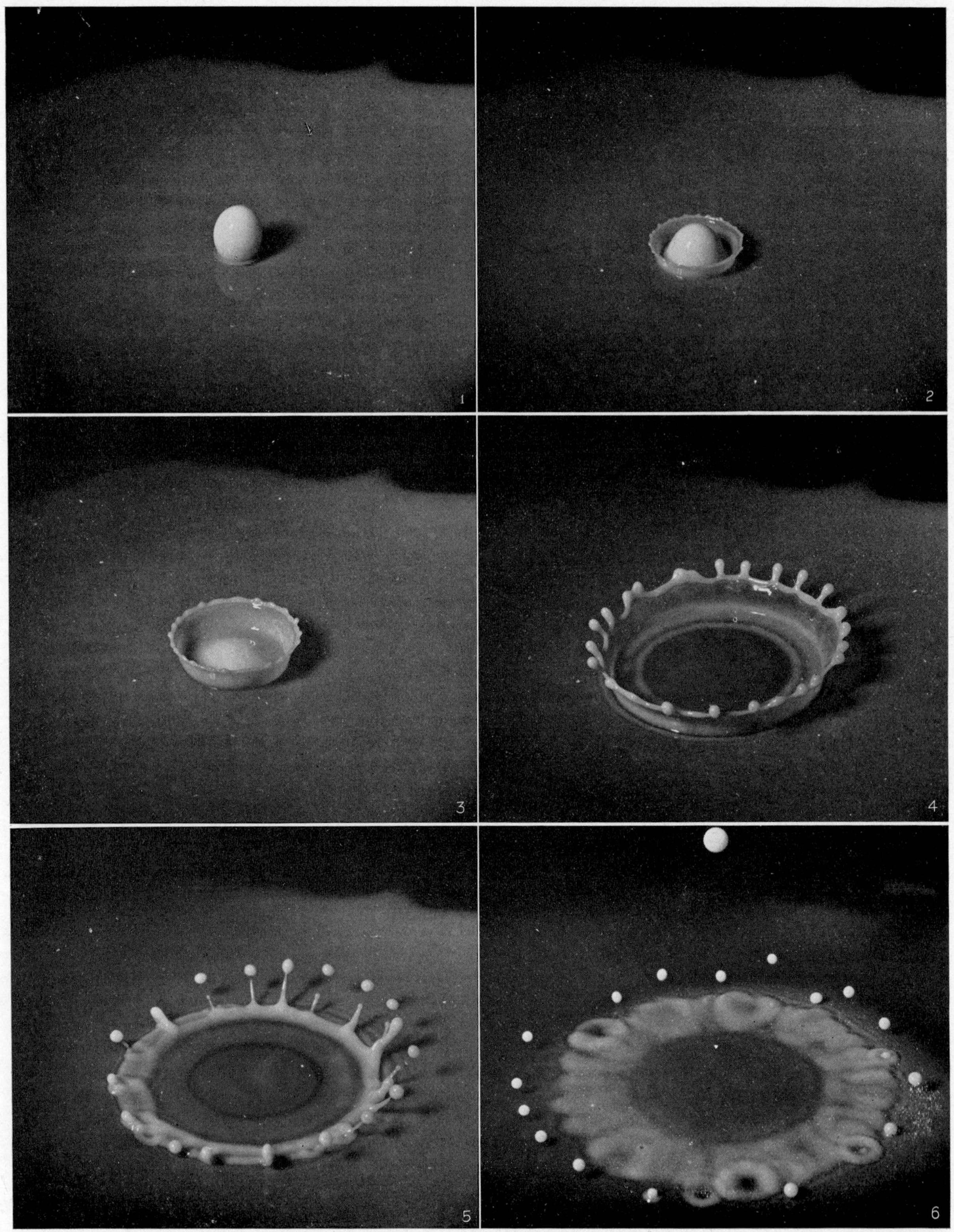

DROP OF MILK SPLASHING ON A PLATE
Showing the crownlike formation of the splash

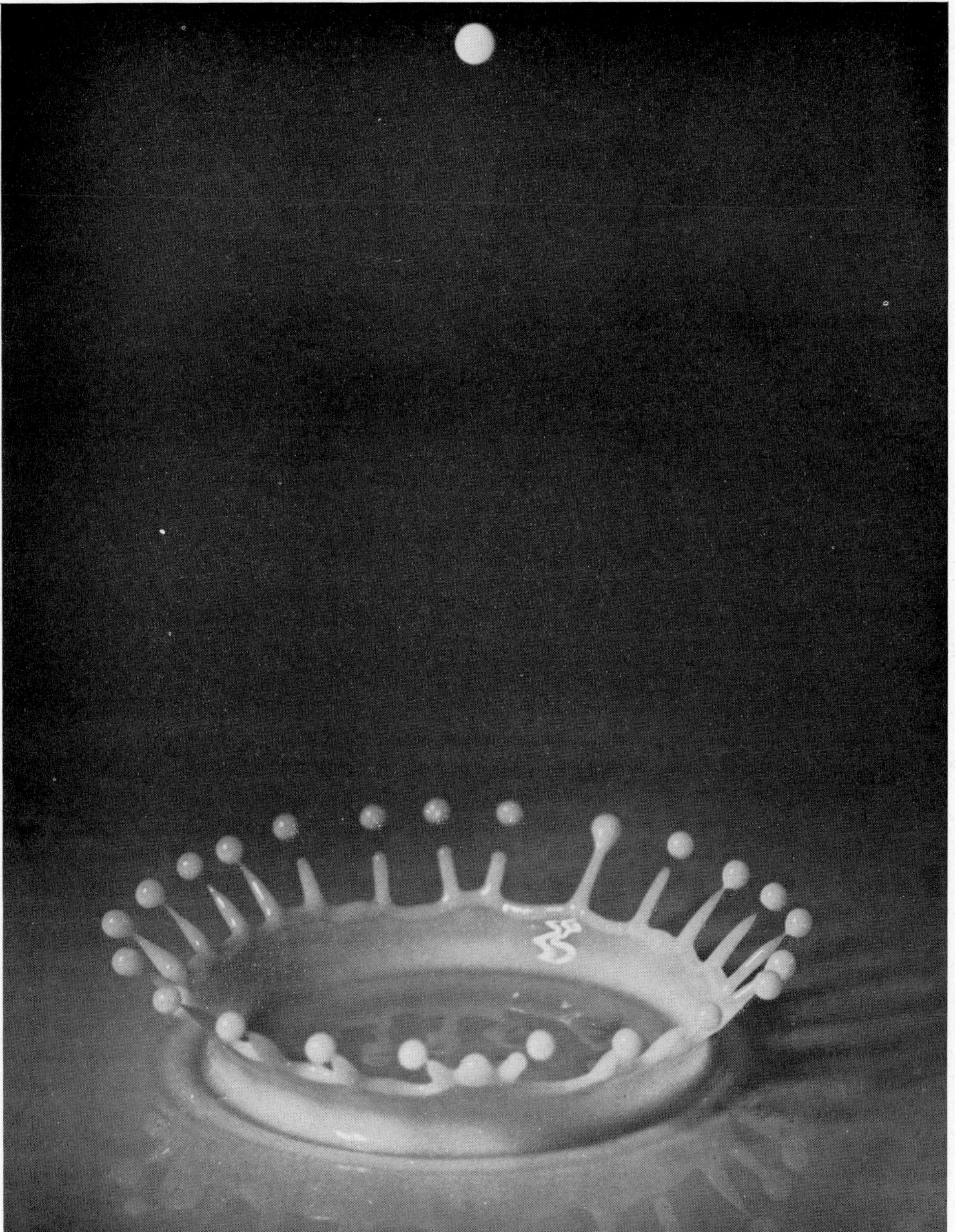

CORONET

Here is a diadem, decorated with pearls raised above the rim, produced by a drop of milk falling upon a plate covered with a thin layer of milk. In the land of splashes, what the scientist knows as Surface Tension is a sculptor in liquids, and fashions from them delicate shapes none the less beautiful because they are too ephemeral for any eye but that of the high-speed camera

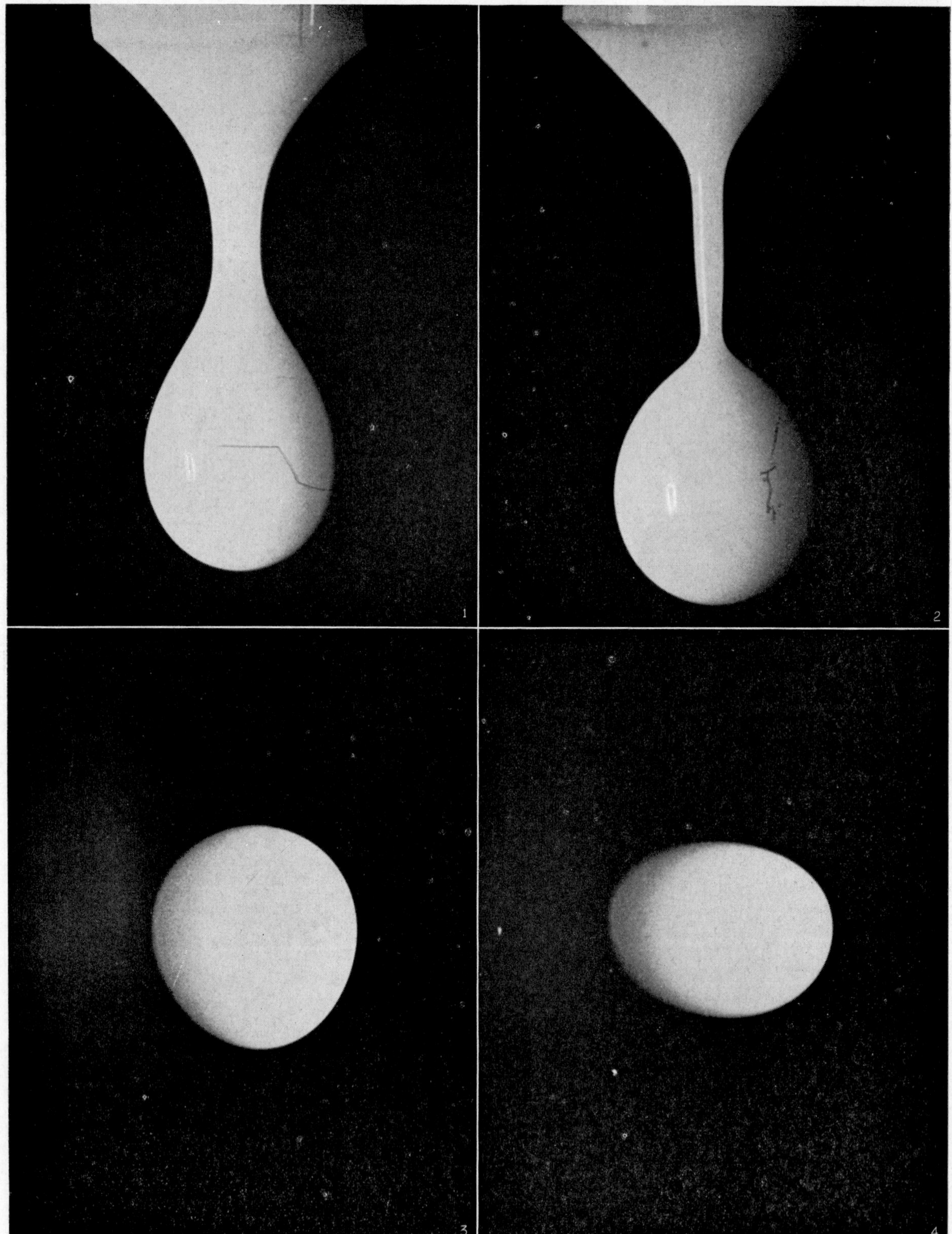

FORMATION OF A DROP. I

Milk dropping from a glass tube in four successive stages. After breaking loose the drop pulsates, tends to assume a stable shape which is not a teardrop. Each picture above and on the opposite page is of a different drop; however, each was taken under the same conditions but at a different distance from the origin

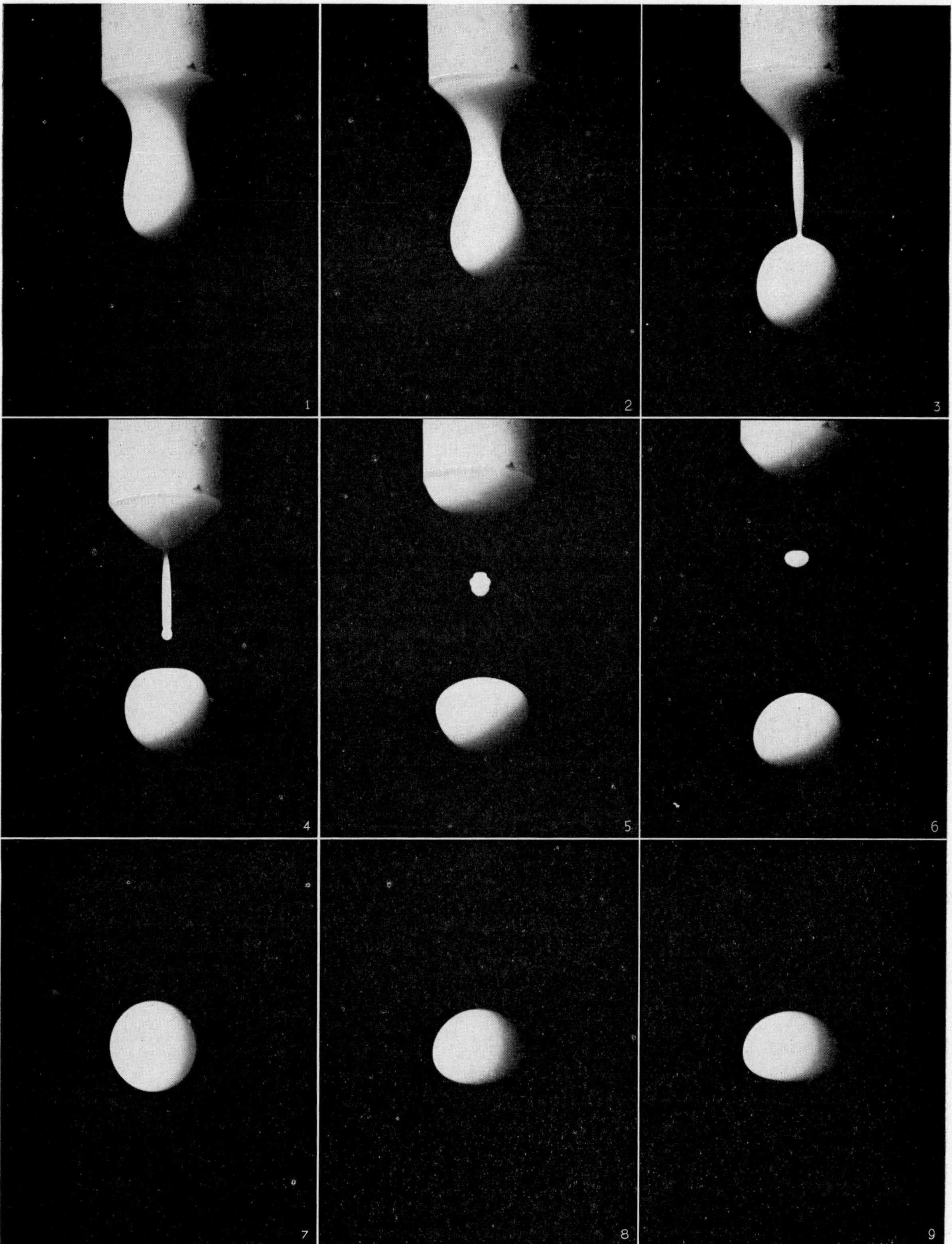

FORMATION OF A DROP. II

A small drop follows the larger and during its oscillations takes the unexpected shape revealed in 5. Picture 8 shows a drop that has fallen six or eight feet. During this fall the oscillations have ceased, and the forces of windage and surface tension gradually reach a balance, resulting in the stable shape shown. The drop in 9 has fallen 14 feet and flattened slightly but has the same contour as the drop in 8

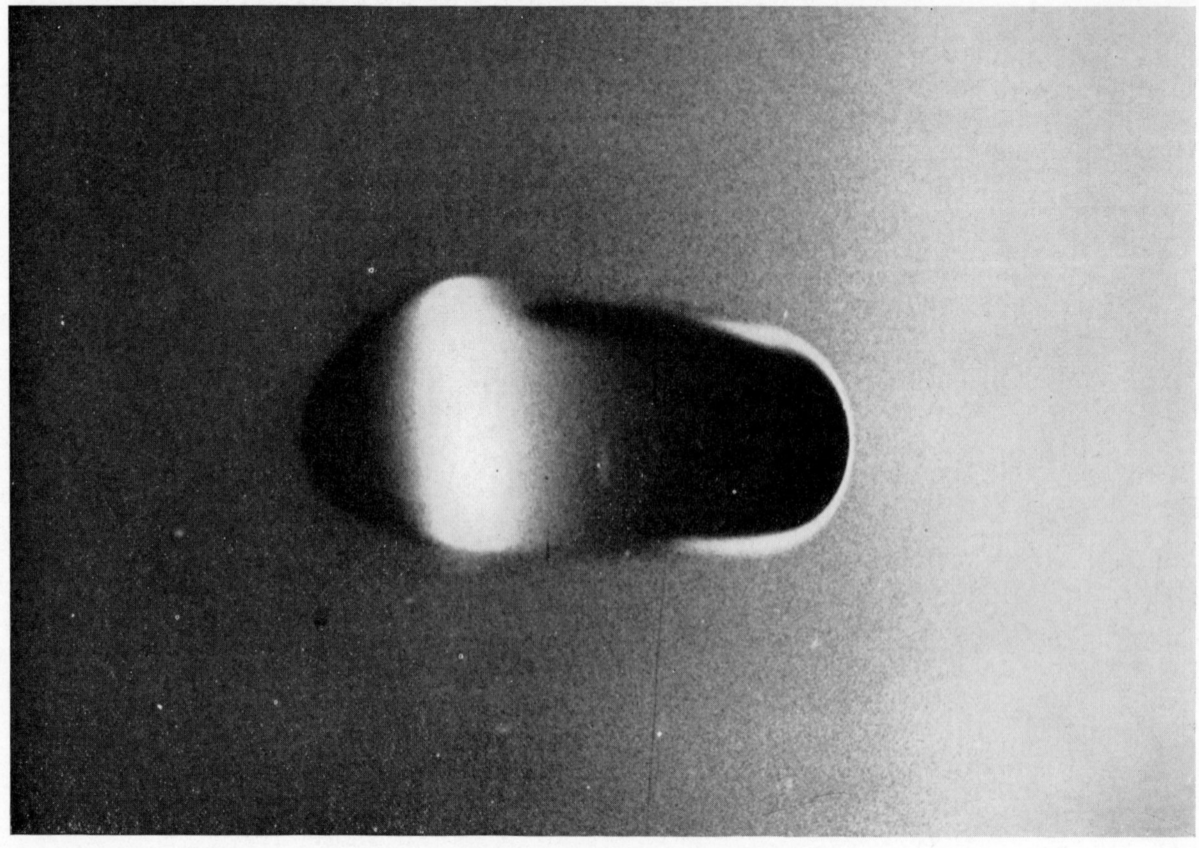

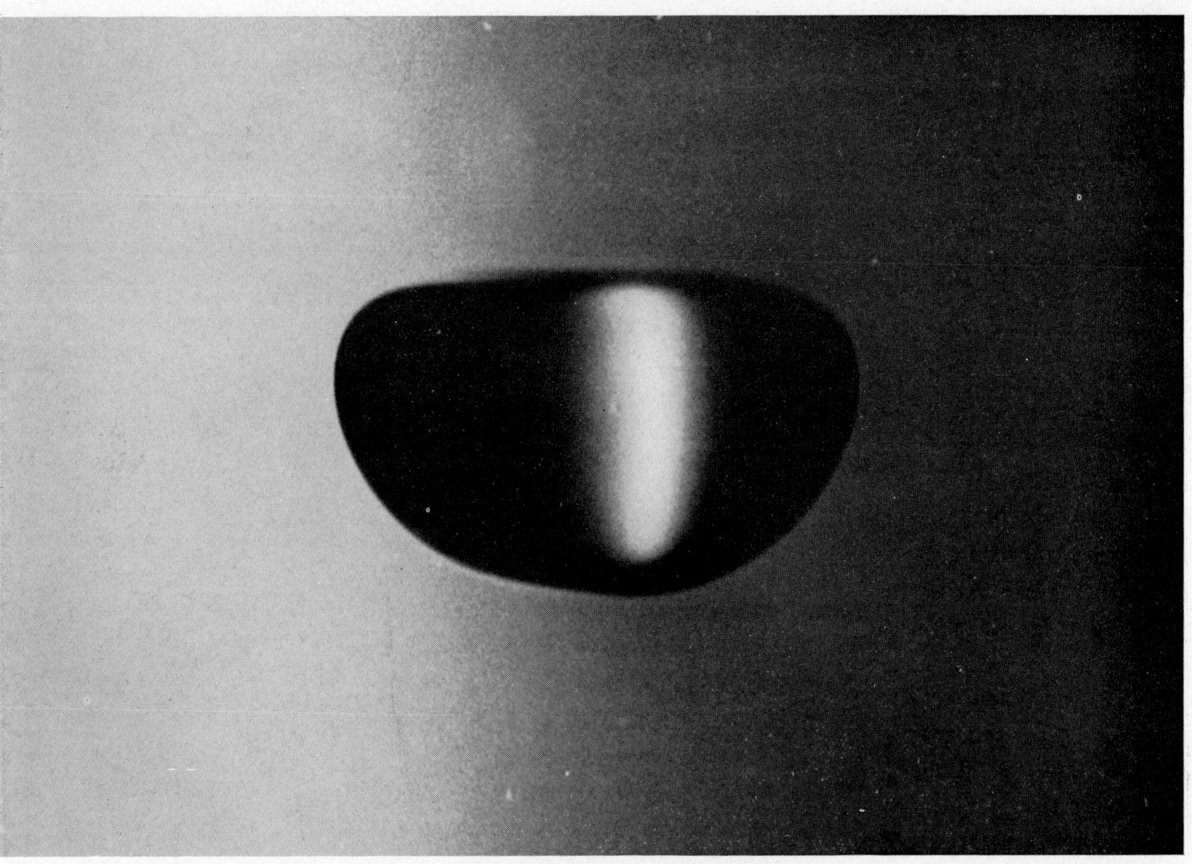

LONG-DISTANCE DROPS

The water drops on the opposite page had fallen three stories, the drop above had fallen eight stories, down an elevator shaft when caught by the high-speed camera. In falling these distances the drops, pulsating as they fall, do not always fall straight but slip sideways after flattening out. After thus slipping, their shapes apparently change, and they start again dropping in a straight line, again flatten out.

Notable in these pictures are the irregular shapes of the drops, the absence of the oft-mentioned teardrop shape

IN A SHOT TOWER

Molten lead congealing into shot as it falls. Out-of-focus reflections of the light source on the drops produce the array of halos

WATER KNIFE

This jet of water is used to cut the pulp on the Fourdrinier wire of a paper machine. The sheet of pulp is moving at a speed of 300 feet a minute

GINGER ALE

SODA WATER

A STREAM OF WATER BECOMES A SERIES OF DROPS . . .

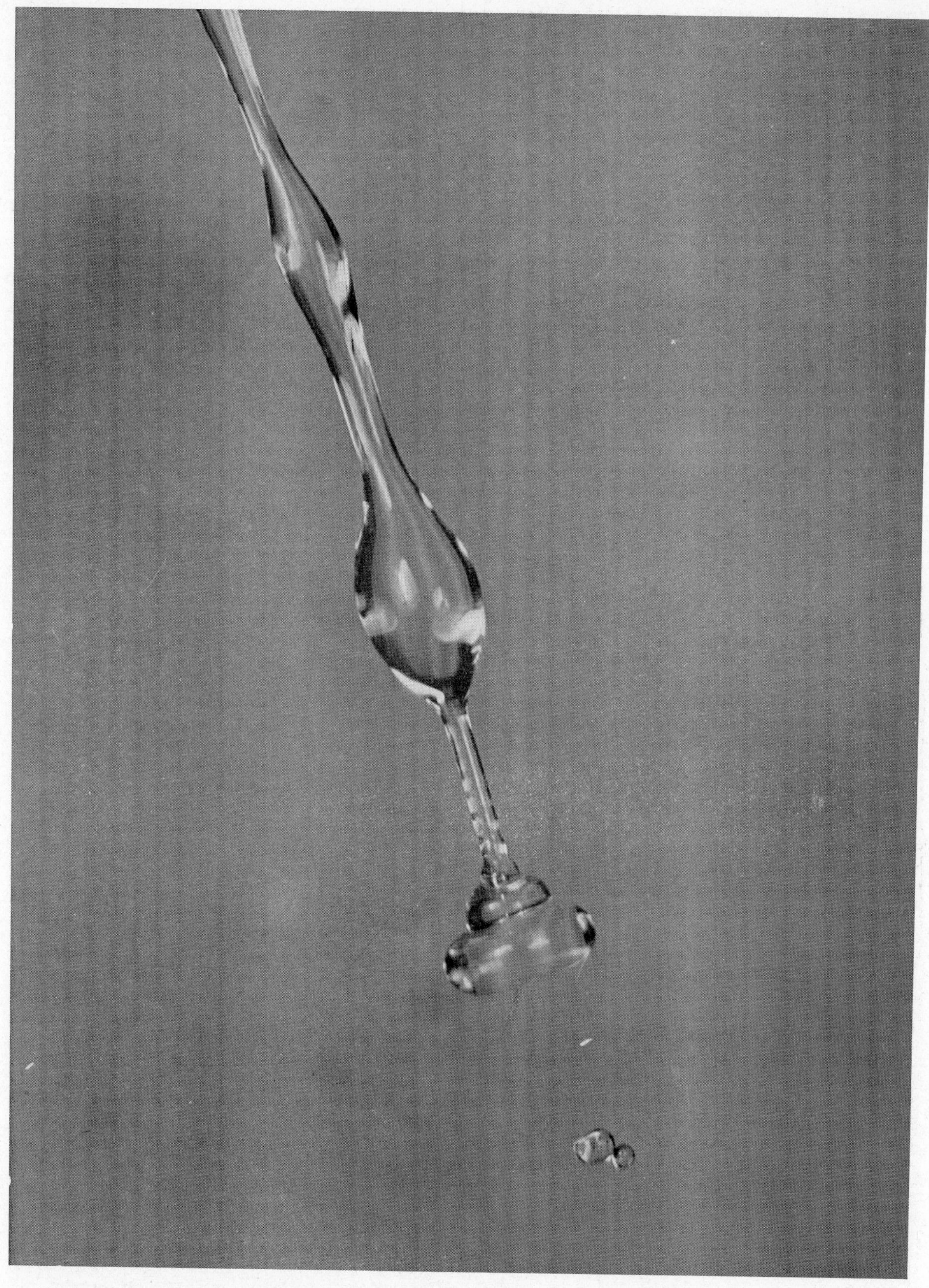

. . . JOINED TOGETHER BY NARROW NECKS OF LIQUID

A LAWN SPRINKLER DRAWS A FIGURE EIGHT

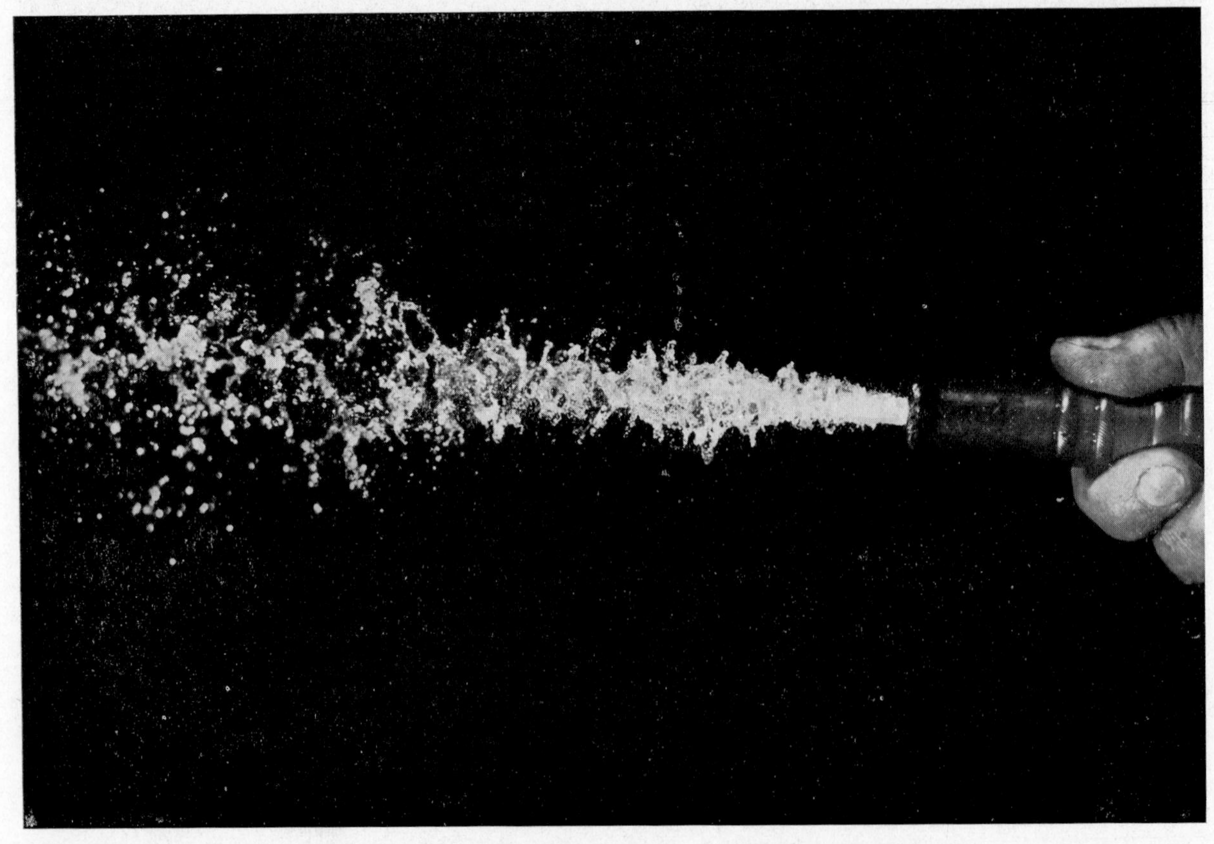

THE TURBULENT STREAM FROM A GARDEN HOSE

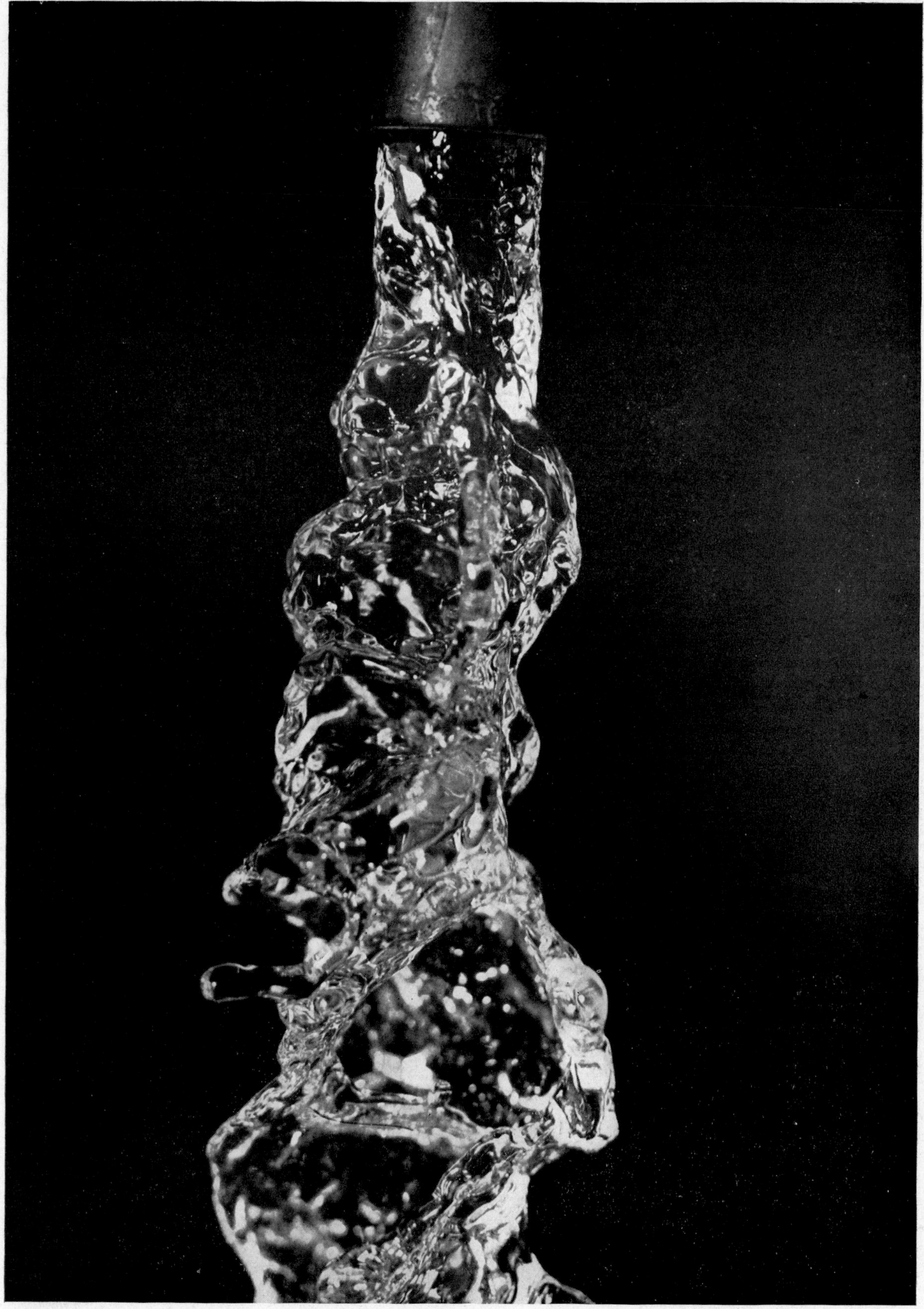

WHAT IS IT?

Ice? Glass? Cellophane? Neither; it is plain tap water flowing from a faucet. Note that the water is streamlined near the faucet but quickly becomes turbulent. In 1/50,000 of a second even this turbulence poses with glassy immobility

THIS IS COFFEE

As the dropped cup hits the floor, a delicate spout leaps upward and coffee slowly oozes through the cracks. The concussion of the cup tripped the contact mechanism which set off the flash

THIS IS MILK

When the glass of milk strikes the floor after falling five feet, pieces of glass fly upward and the milk seems to flow out with molasseslike deliberation

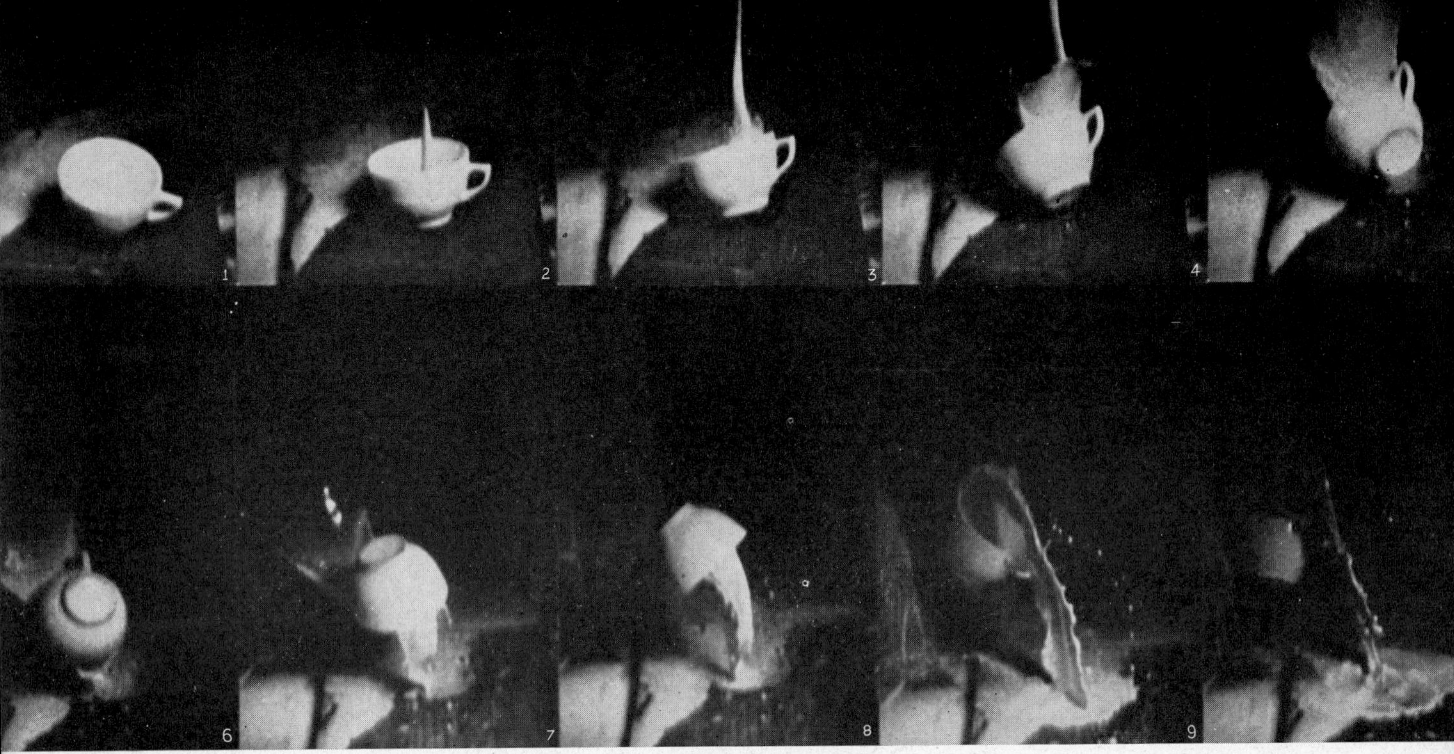

THE TUMBLING CUP

Here the cup refused to break when it struck the floor, this time wood rather than terrazzo as on the two previous pages. Instead it staged a tumbling act. In scene 1 the cup is just hitting the floor; in 2 it is beginning to bounce, and the milk it contains shoots up, geyserlike; in 3 the somersault is started and the geyser climbs higher; and in the succeeding pictures the geyser fans out and the cup turns completely over and spills its contents before it finally comes to rest

WATER WHEEL
The action of a jet of water impinging on the buckets of a Pelton wheel

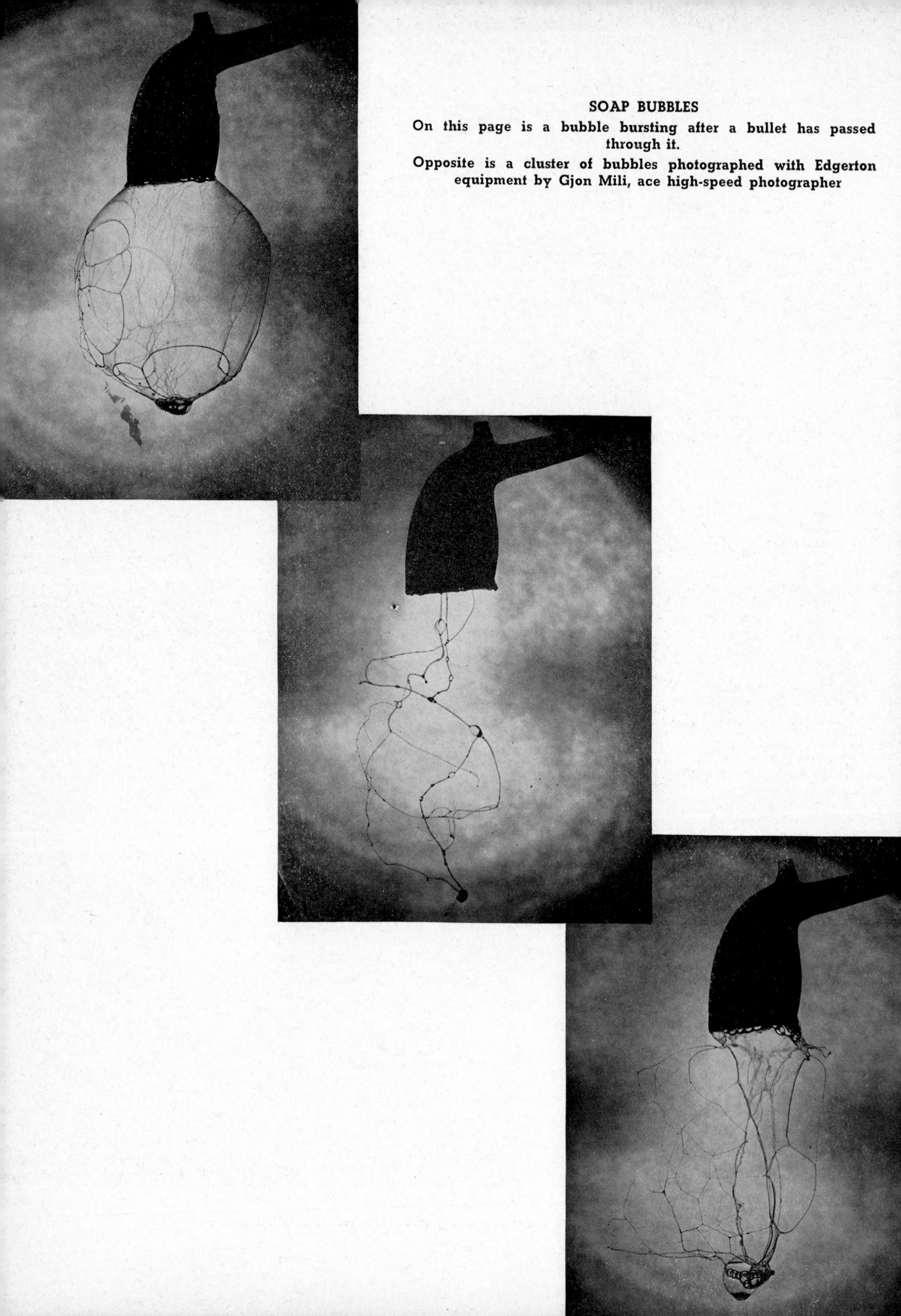

SOAP BUBBLES

On this page is a bubble bursting after a bullet has passed through it.

Opposite is a cluster of bubbles photographed with Edgerton equipment by Gjon Mili, ace high-speed photographer

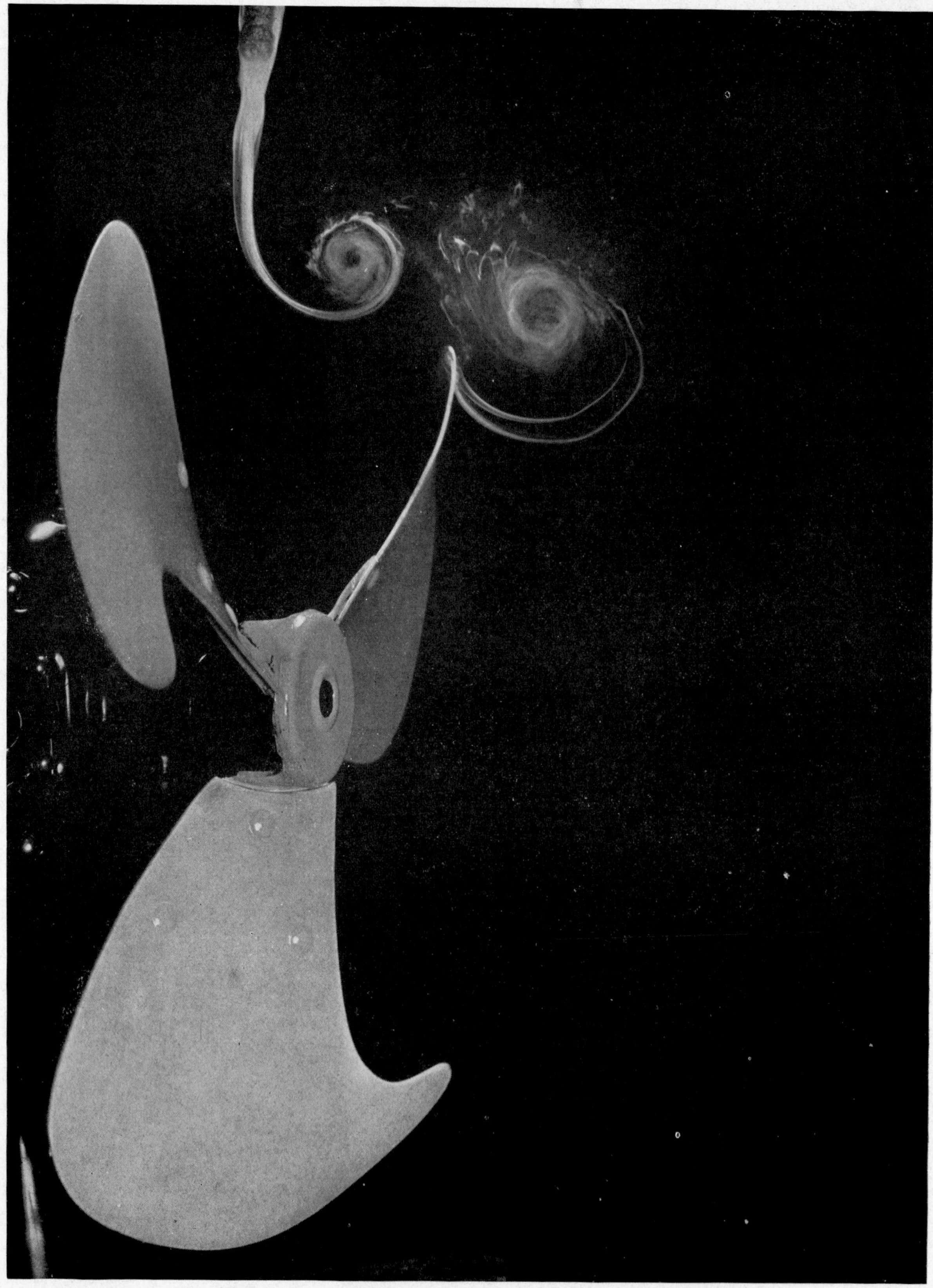

THE FAN IS TURNING 2,000 REVOLUTIONS A MINUTE
By using smoky titanium tetrachloride we can see the vortices in the air caused by the whirling fan. Such effects may be seen directly by the eye when stroboscopic light illuminates the fan

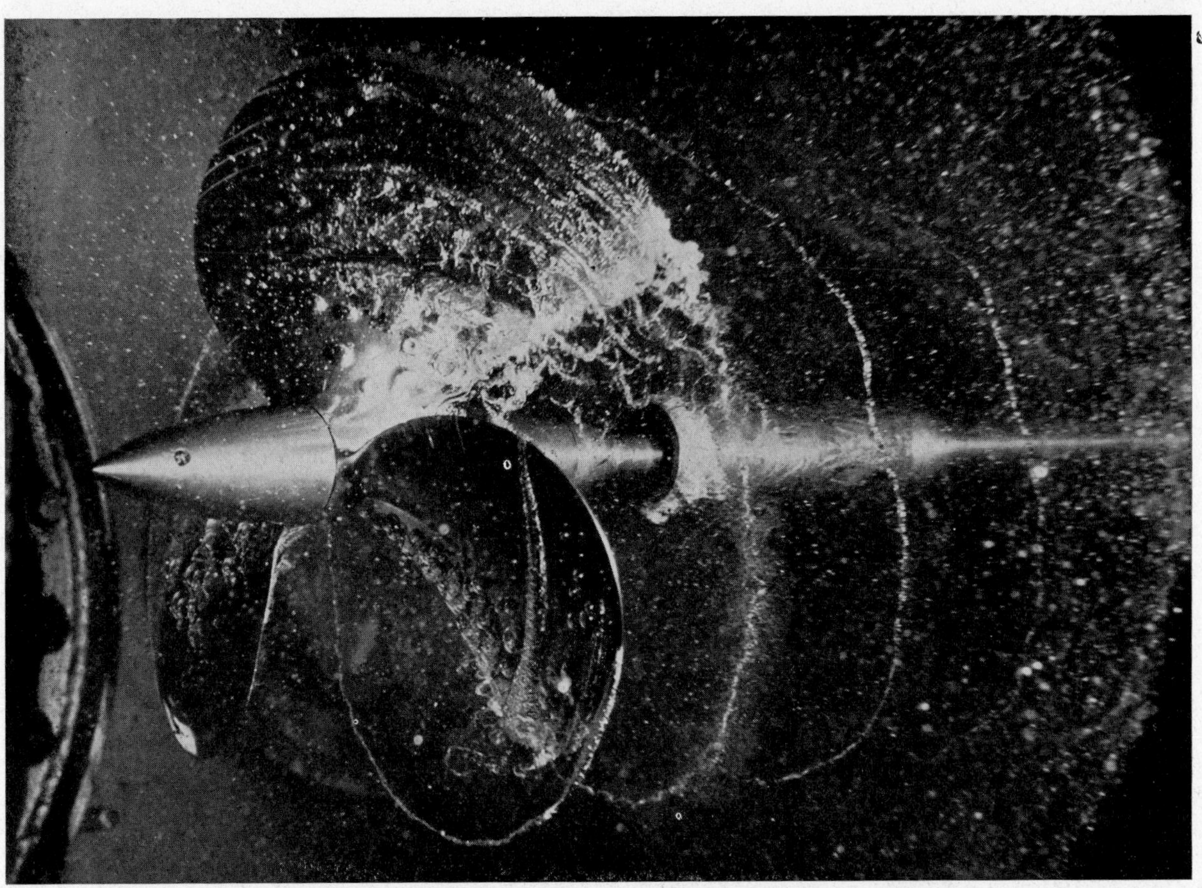

THE ACTION OF WATER ABOUT A REVOLVING SHIP'S PROPELLER

To aid in the design of better screws the Massachusetts Institute of Technology has recently built a propeller tank within which screws may be tested and observed in operation. Here is a typical view under stroboscopic light of a propeller rapidly revolving in water. The implosive bubbles which have a destructive action (cavitation) on propellers may be seen here

IN THE SERVICE OF SCIENCE AND INDUSTRY

High-speed photography is by no means a stunt, useful only for obtaining trick effects. It is rapidly becoming one of the most versatile tools of the scientist and engineer, who use it to reveal hidden phenomena, to measure velocities, to detect distortion that needs to be eliminated. The high-speed camera has been used—to mention only several of its many practical applications—to make better propellers and fans, to look into engine cylinders in order to help in solving the problem of knock, to study the spray from a Diesel-engine jet, to aid the designer of automatic machines, and to help the engineer in improving manufacturing processes.

On this and the pages immediately following are reproduced a few prints made for technical purposes, simply by way of emphasizing this less spectacular but more important function of the high-speed technique.

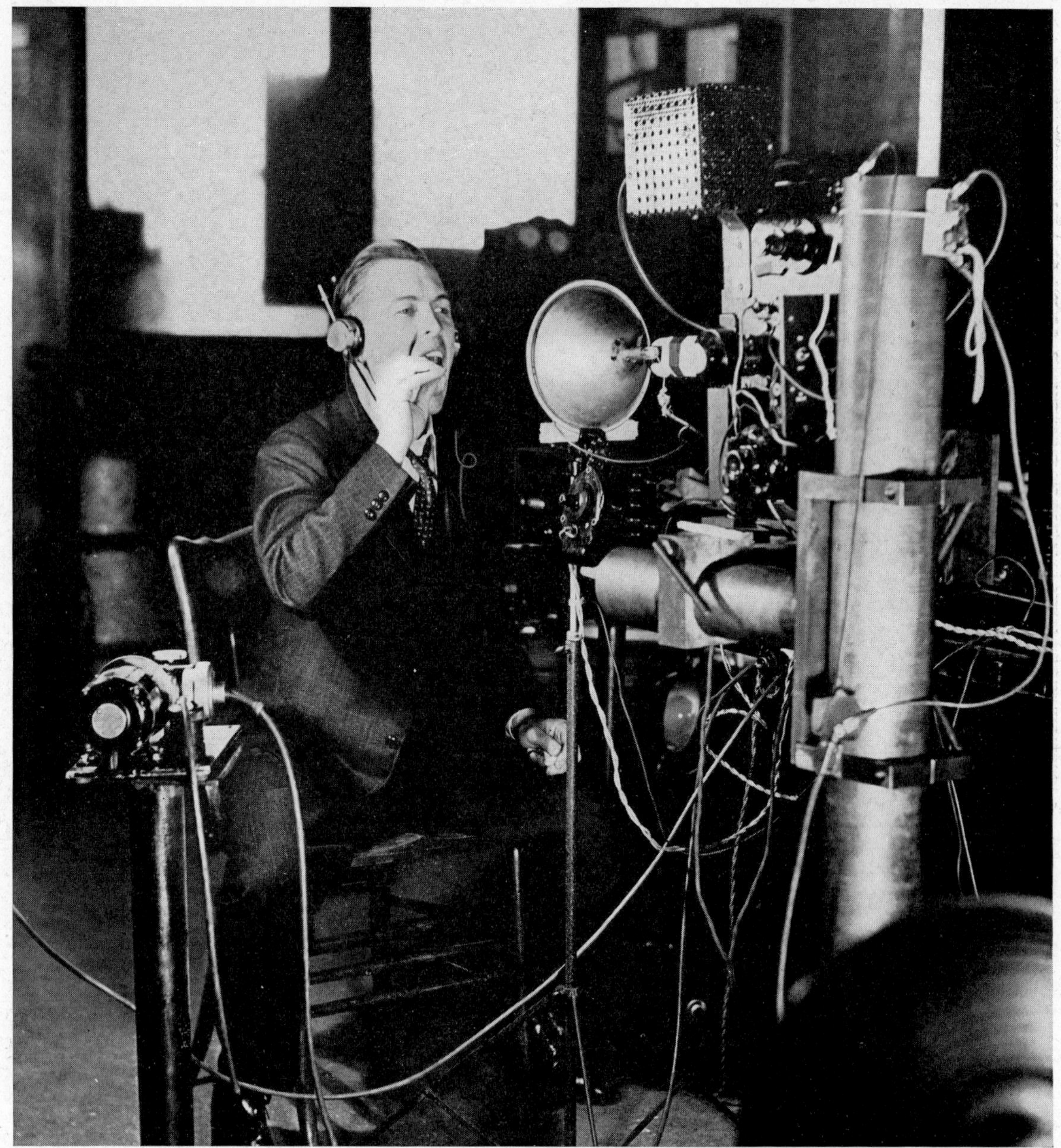

Here is how Dr. Moore posed for vocal-fold pictures. He is looking directly into the light, and the camera is mounted behind the light

INTO THE HUMAN THROAT WITH THE HIGH-SPEED CAMERA

Have you ever seen a voice making a noise? Lip reading, yes, but the lips and tongue control the shape of the sound, transpose it into the code we have adopted for social usage. The sound itself originates behind the tongue in the almost inaccessible region above the Adam's apple. More specifically, pitch and volume are controlled by the opening between, and the movements of, the vocal folds.

For some years scientists have been trying to photograph these folds in an attempt to learn the direction or directions of their movement, the relationship between the two folds, the effect of changing pitch and altering vocal intensity. A step forward, which should be of value to doctors as well as scientists, has

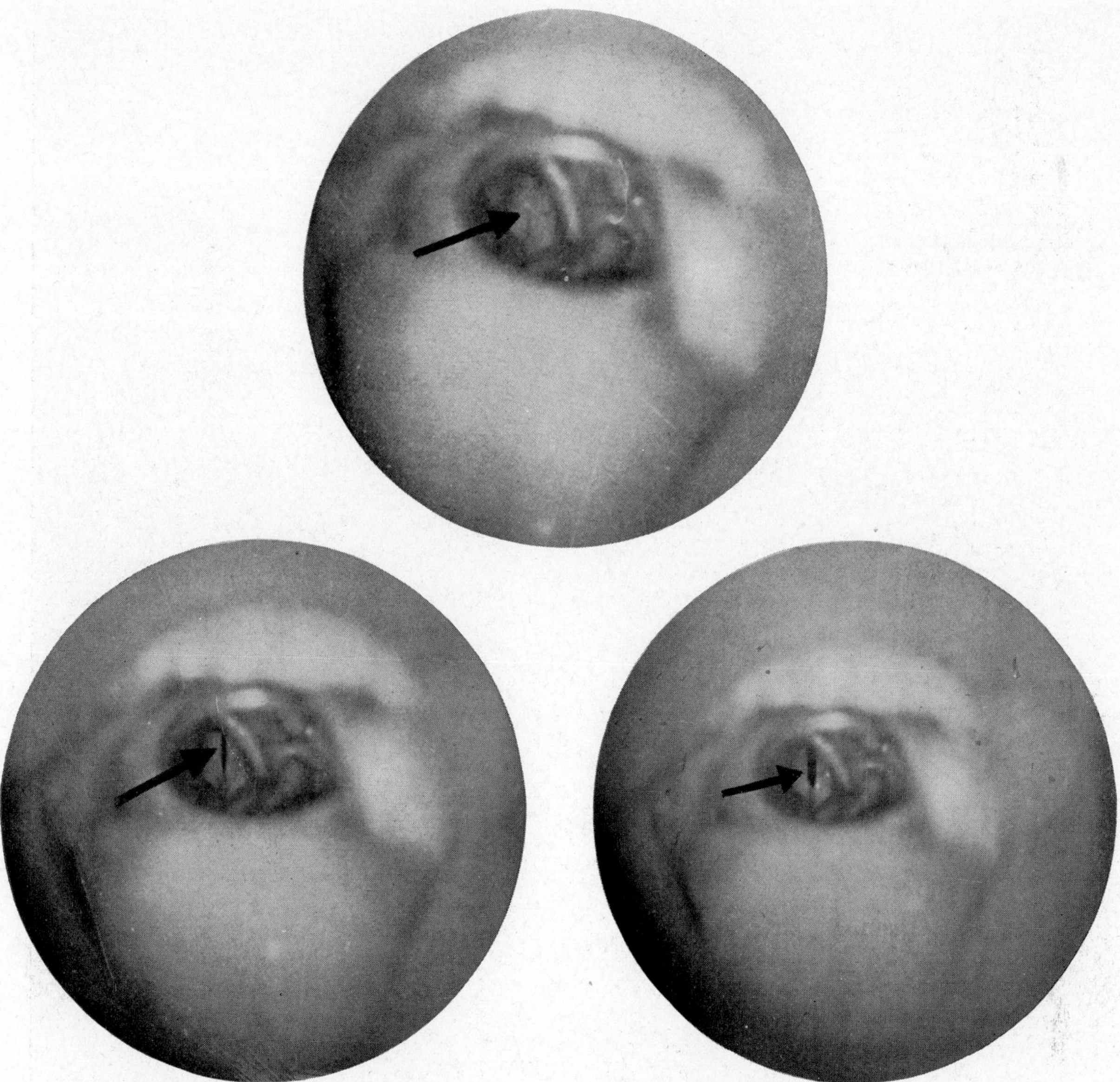

SEEING SONG AT ITS SOURCE

In the photographs above the arrow points to the vocal folds, which may be seen in three different stages of vibration. In the upper picture, they are touching each other; in the lower left picture, a partial opening shows; and in the photograph on the right the folds are widely separated. Amplitude of movement varies with the pitch and intensity, i.e., greater intensity parallels larger excursions, other factors unchanged, while lessened amplitude accompanies rise in pitch. The hazy circle around the enlarged center can be recognized as the subject's teeth and tongue slightly out of focus

been made recently, however, through the use of the laryngoscope perfected by Dr. Paul Moore of Northwestern University. Dr. Moore's laryngoscope directs the light from a stroboscope down to the vocal folds and back again, over the same path, to the camera.

Recently Dr. Moore brought his apparatus to Cambridge for use with the stroboscope. Motion pictures were taken of Dr. Moore, shown opposite holding in his mouth a guttural mirror and facing the stroboscopic camera. The mirror directs the rays and reflects the light beams to the area to be photographed. The camera is focused through a hole in the back of the stroboscopic lamp reflector so that the light reflected from the folds can use the same optical path as the incoming light. Earphones give the tone that is to be voiced by the subject.

SPINNING
Thread in a ring traveler spinning at 10,000 revolutions a minute.
The effects of centrifugal force and windage are apparent

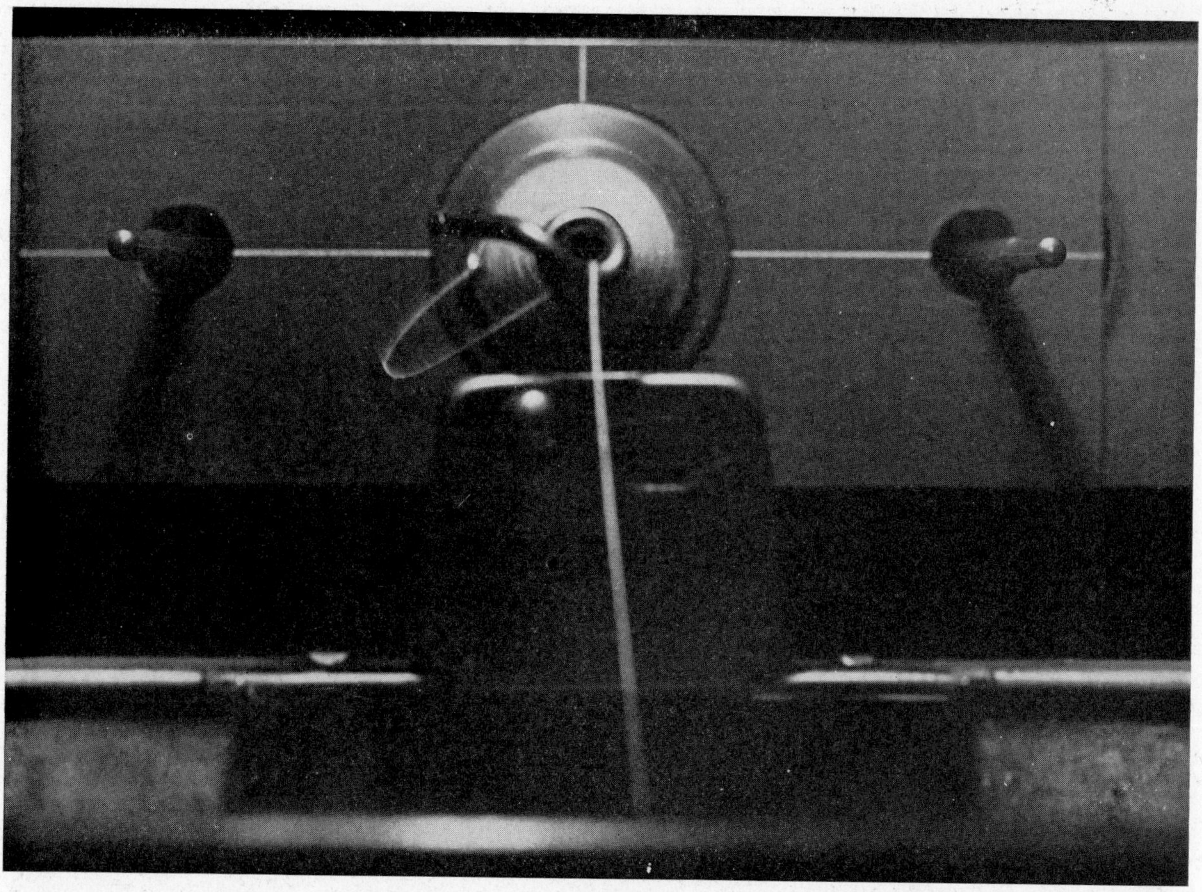

AT 10,000 R.P.M.

From above is seen the lag angle of the thread resulting from windage

WEAVING

The flying shuttle is just entering the "shed" made by the warp threads, and is taking up the slack in the loop of the filling, or transverse, thread. Note the twist in the filling.
This is one of a series of pictures made in a study of loom action to discover why the filling thread sometimes breaks and the shuttle occasionally flies out of line and tears into the warp threads

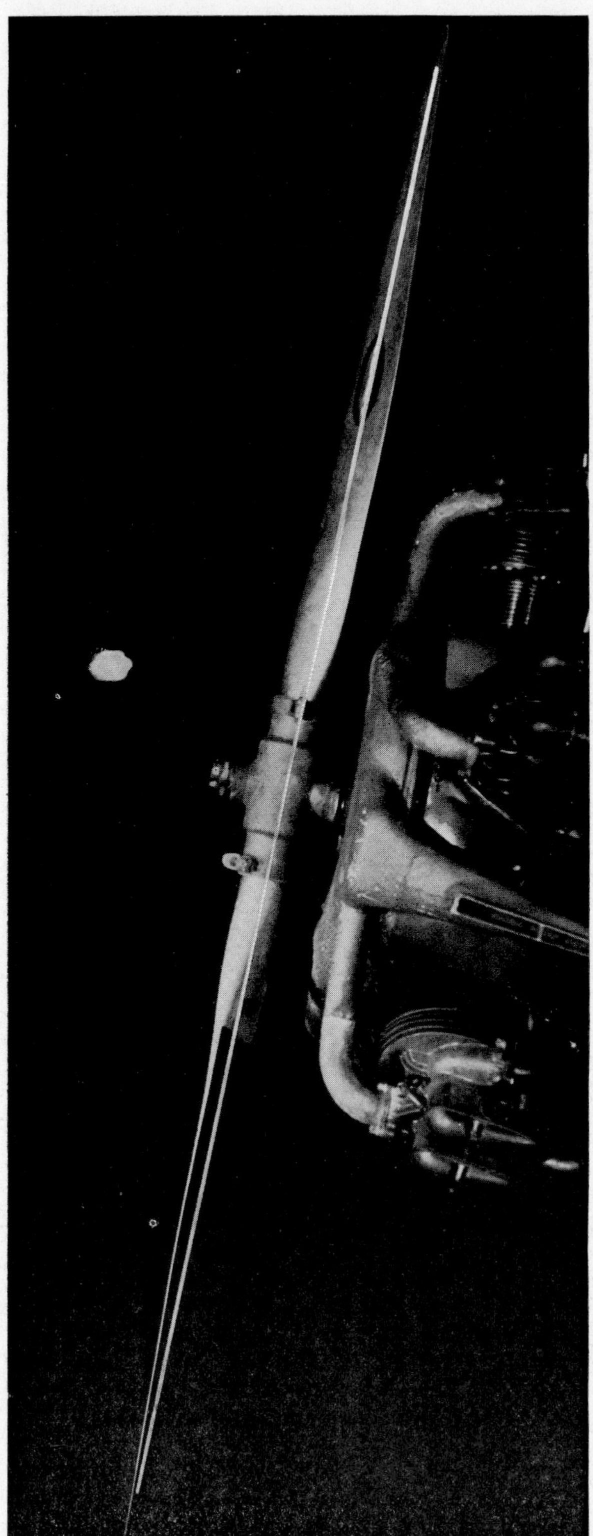

THE PROP BENDS

On the left the propeller is standing still and, as indicated by the white line, there is no deflection. In the right view, the propeller, whirling at full speed, deflects as it bites the air.

Such study of deflection in fast-moving objects is one of the many engineering uses of the stroboscope and high-speed camera

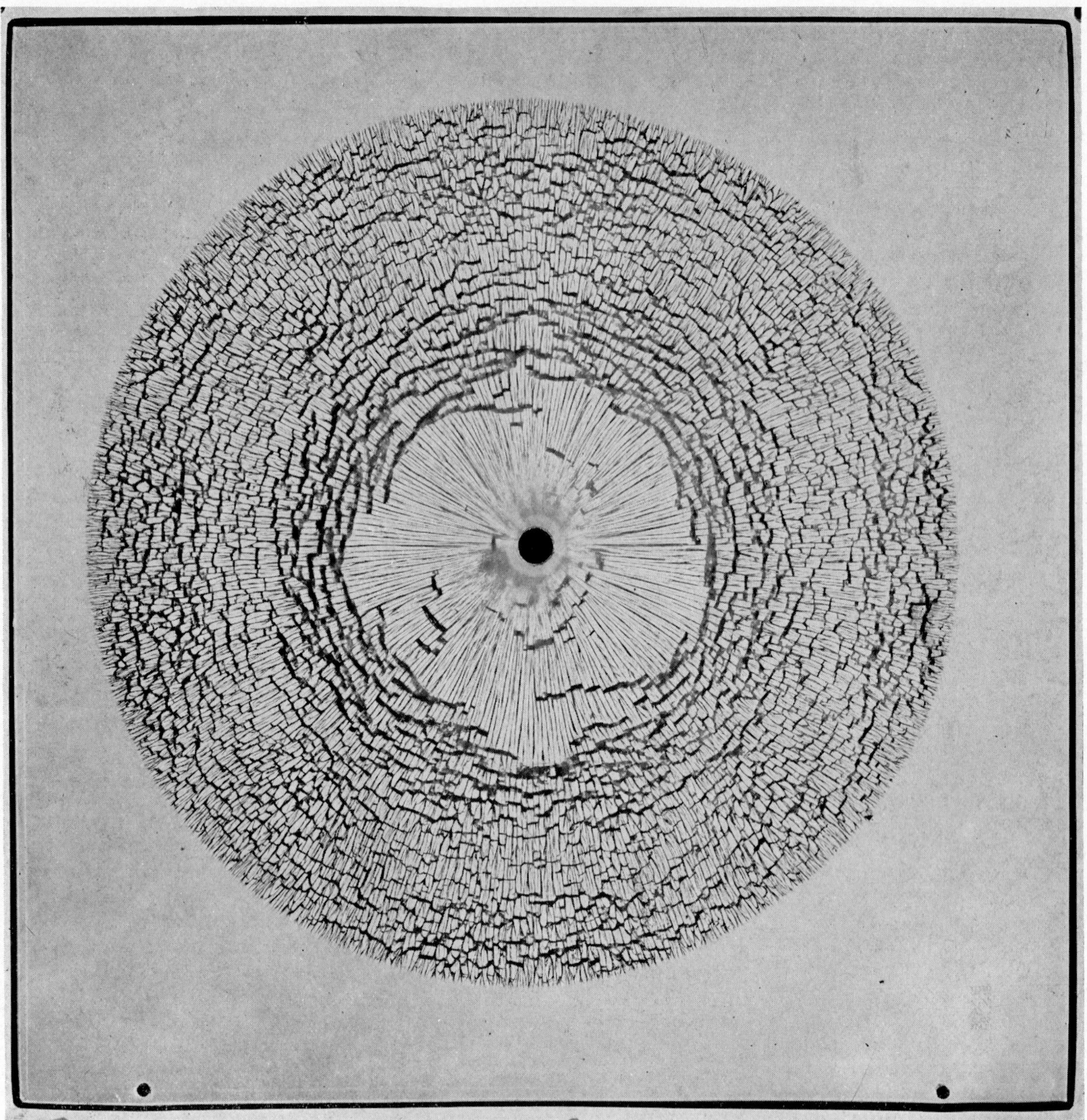

HOW FAST DOES GLASS CRACK?

This is not an idle riddle; it is a matter of concern to makers and users of glass, for an understanding answer might aid in making a stronger bottle, a safer safety glass. The adjacent pictures are drawn from a series taken to determine not only how fast glass cracks but how it cracks.

The technique of taking these pictures is essentially this: A spring-driven metal plunger strikes the glass with enough force to break it and in doing so starts an electrical timing circuit which at the proper split second sets off an electric flash and exposes the negative, the exposure being less than one-millionth of a second. So accurate and responsive to control is the timing that a crack

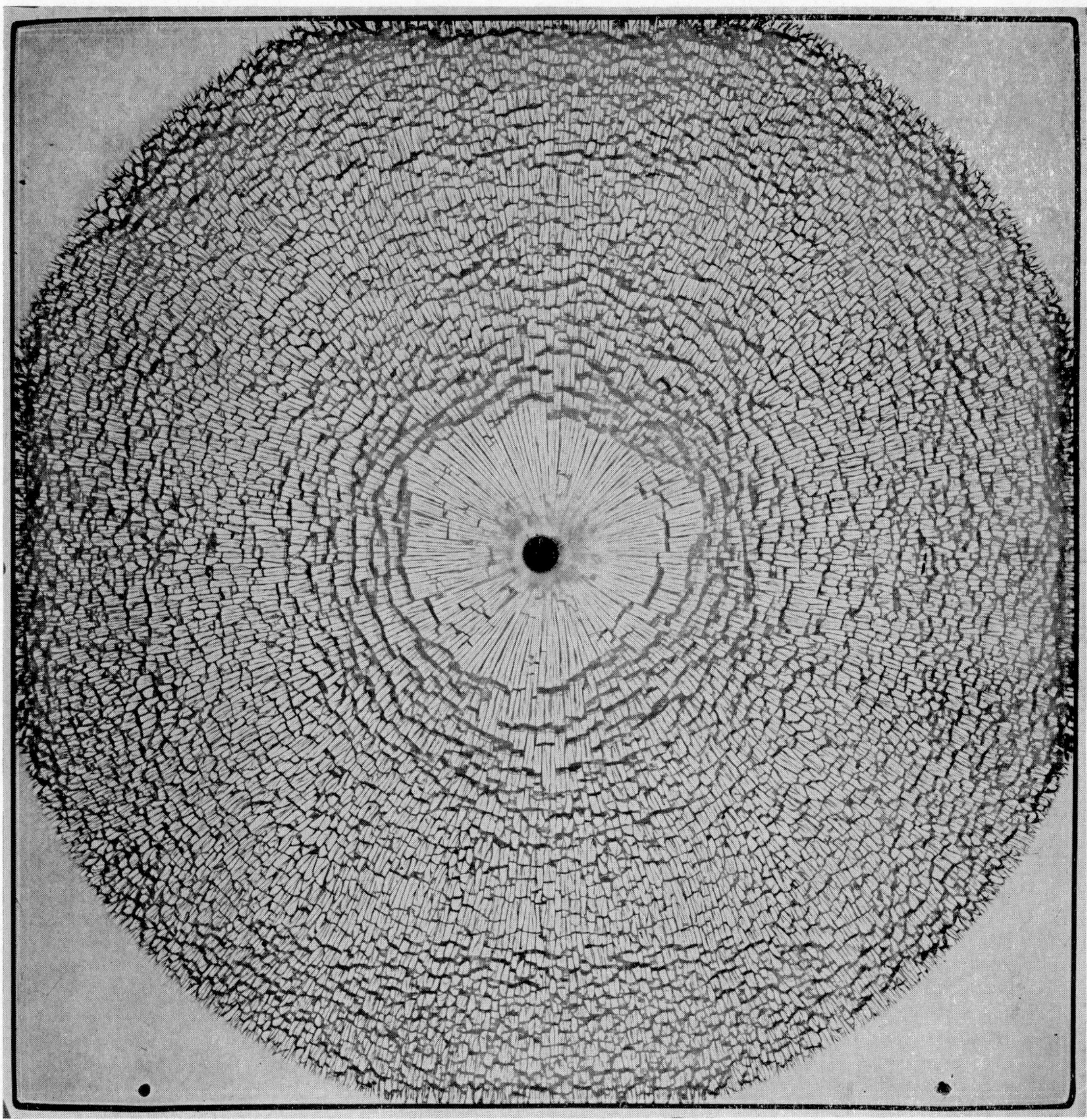

moving at nearly a mile a second can be stopped dead in its tracks at any desired point—as the two pictures at the top of these pages show.

This high-speed photographic method of studying the propagation of glass cracks has been carried out by Graduate Student Frederick E. Barstow of the Massachusetts Institute of Technology's Department of Physics, working under the direction of Professor Edgerton. The cracking speed of 5,000 feet a second obtained by the German investigator, Professor H. Schardin, who used bullets, has been checked by Barstow and Edgerton, and their data indicate that the rate of cracking is independent of the rate of application of the breaking force and that it is the same for both plate and tempered glass.

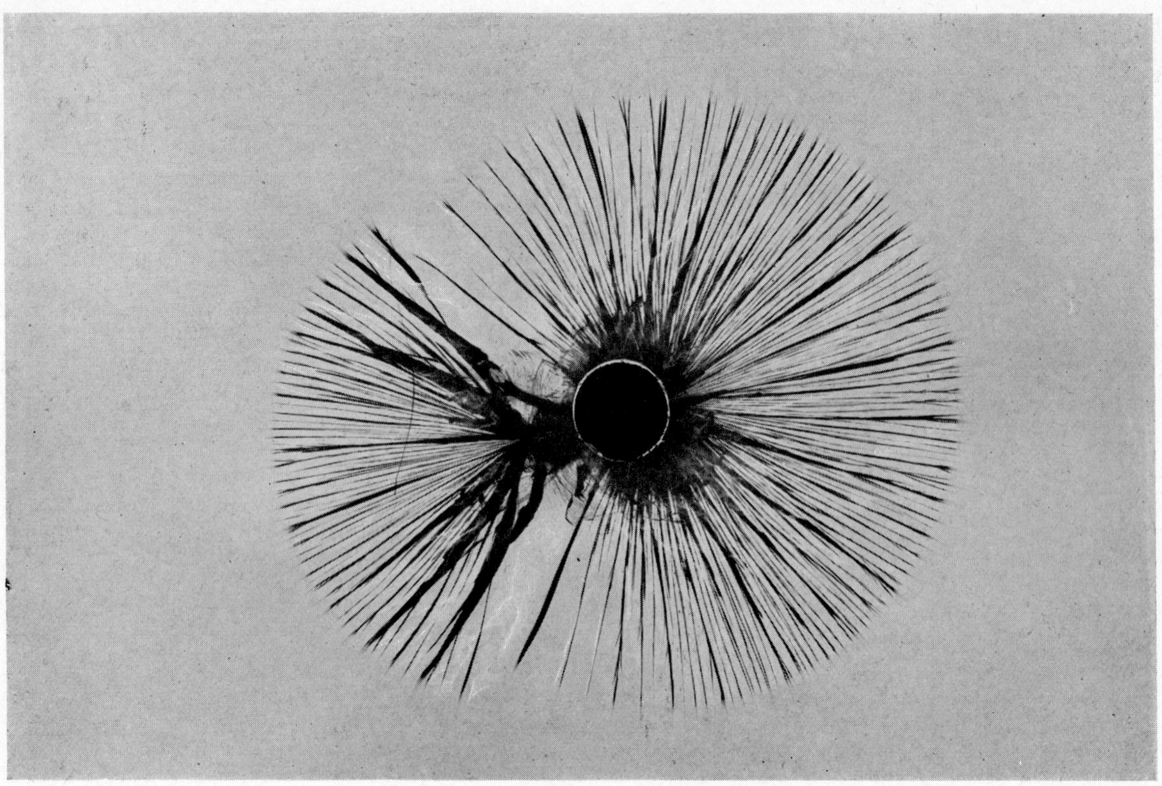

Above. An imperfection in the glass probably caused the glass to assume this exceptional asymmetrical formation.

Below. Here the stresses set up by a plunger hitting the glass start cracks forming at the edge of the plate

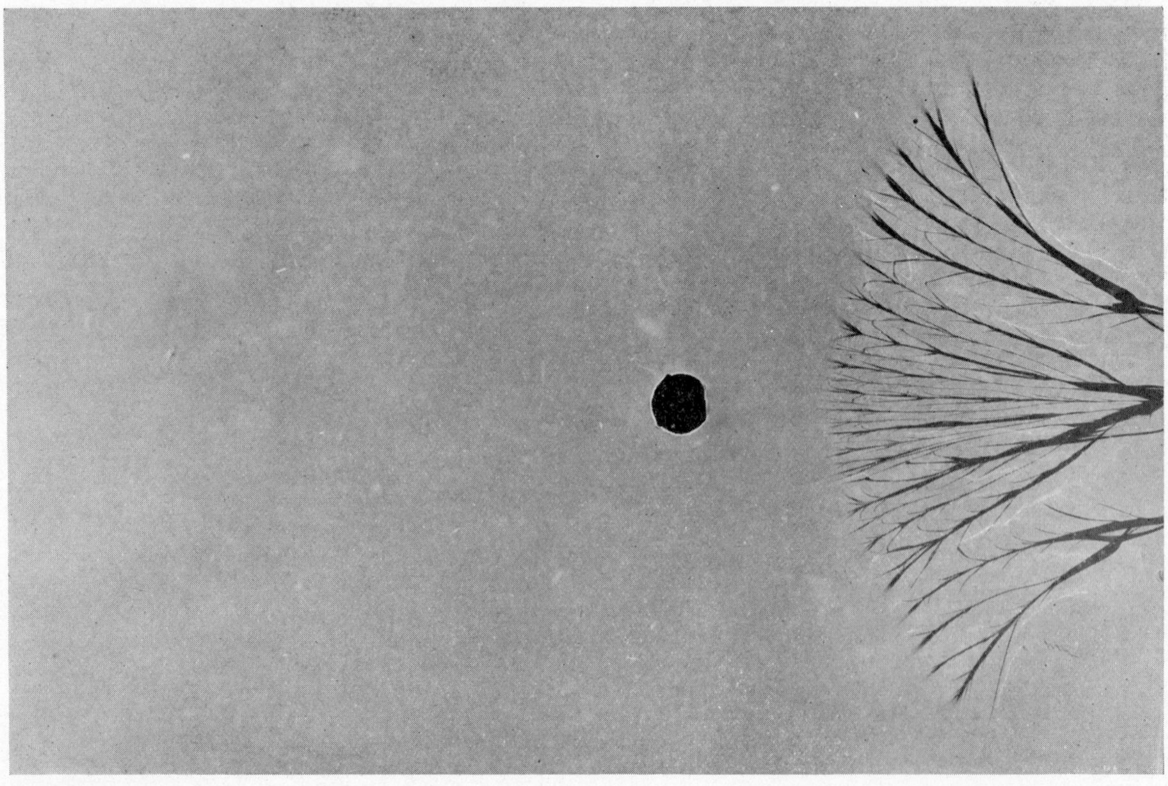

SEEING THE STRAINS IN CRACKING GLASS

These polarized-light photographs, taken with an exposure of less than 1/1,000,000 of a second, show the strains in cracking glass. In the picture above, the glass plate has been struck near the left bottom edge and is cracking near the right

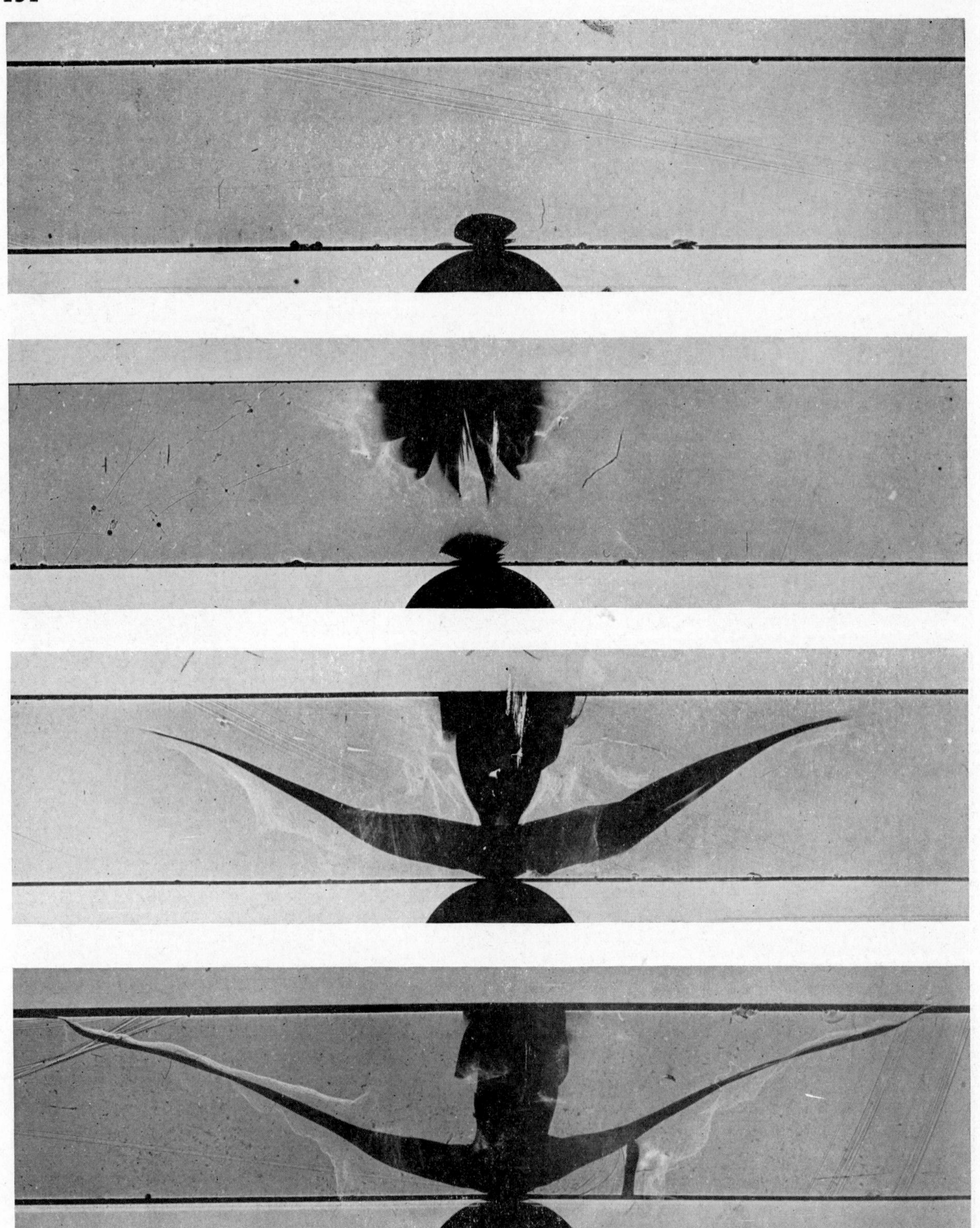

GLASS PLATES CRACKING

Edgewise views of plates cracking (each view is of a different piece of glass at a different stage). The rounded top of the plunger used to break the glass may be seen in contact with the lower side of the plate, and below it in succession are three stages in the mile-a-second progress of the cracking

SMASH!

In stroboscopic light this light bulb seems to be cracking up rather leisurely under the blow of the hammer. The exposure of this picture is only 1/100,000 of a second contrasted to 1/3,000,000 of a second for the glass pictures on the preceding pages. The top of the bulb has been driven inside by the rush of air as the vacuum is broken. The fragments are seen coming out at the bottom

ULTRASPEED MOTION PICTURES

These sequences show the action which occurs when a bullet is fired through tin cans filled with water. In each series the water spouts upward and the can bursts its seam as a result of the bullet plowing through the center. The bullet is visible in only one of the pictures in each strip.

These pictures, taken at the rate of 1,000 a second, are examples of high-speed motion pictures as contrasted with the single-flash or multiple-exposure photography used to make a majority of the other photographs in this book.

When these high-speed motion pictures are projected at standard speeds, we see ultraslow motion which the standard motion-picture speeds could never reveal

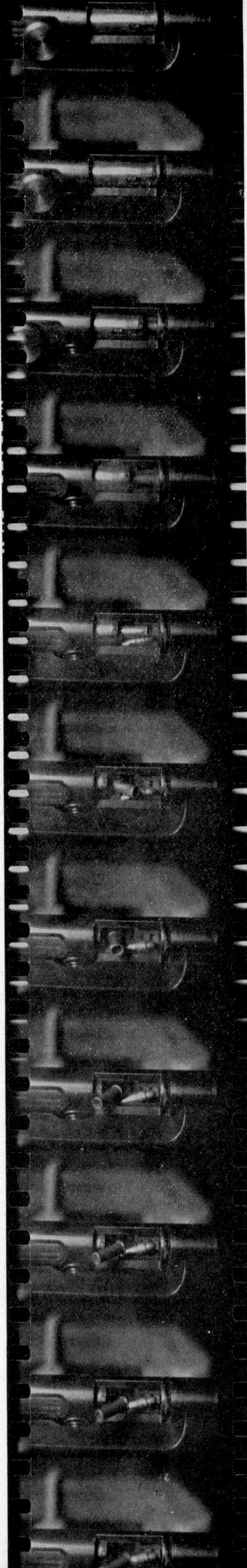

Left. As a .22 semiautomatic is fired, the empty cartridge is ejected and a new cartridge springs into place

Right. Compare this sequence of a .22 automatic pistol with that of the rifle on the left. The interval of time between pictures is 1/600 of a second. The kickup of the muzzle may be seen

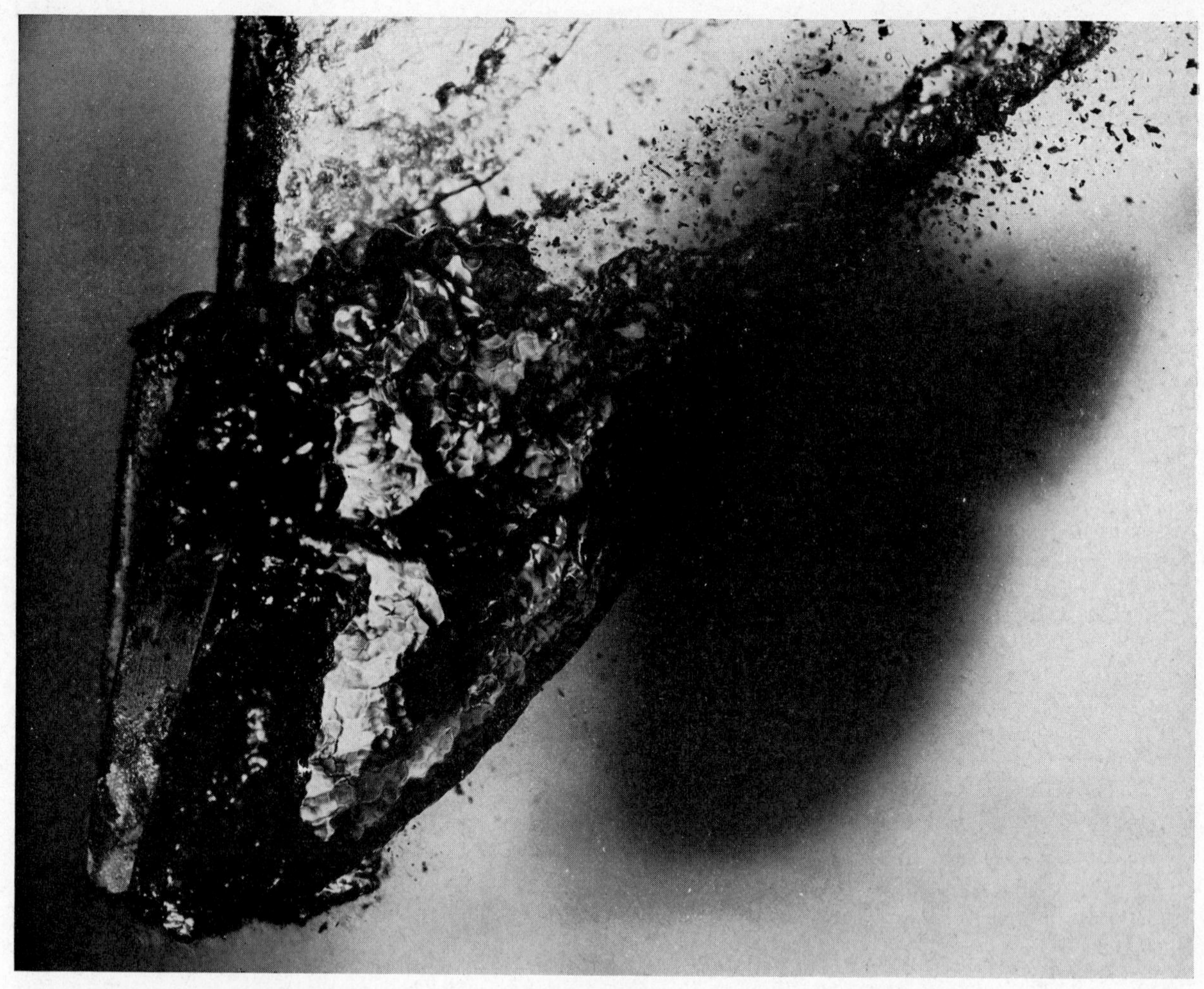

QUENCHING

When steel is quenched—that is to say, cooled—its hardness, or temper, is affected. Different liquids seem to produce different effects. To understand the process better and to put it on a more rational basis, I. N. Zavarine, metallurgist, has been photographing quenching operations at high speed with results shown above, opposite, and on page 160.

The two adjacent photographs show hot steel being plunged into liquids and the turbulence that ensues. At the right note the pretty vortices, the bubbles of gas near the metal, insulating it and hindering the cooling

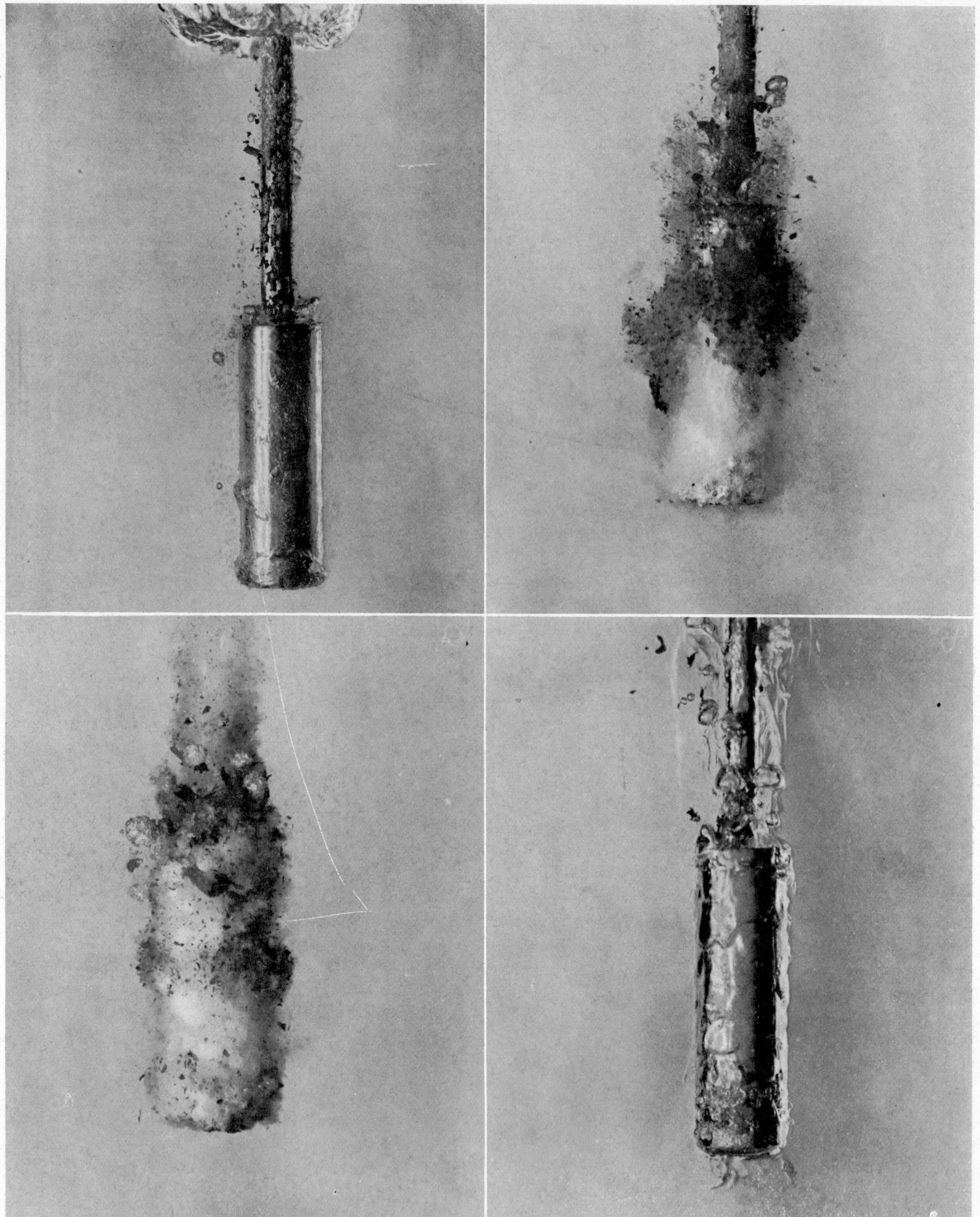

QUENCHING, CONT.

Here a piece of metal heated to 850 degrees C. is plunged into four different solutions, and the action that occurs at the beginning of the quenching process may be clearly seen. The liquid in the upper left picture is water; in the upper right, a 5 per cent solution of NaCl; in the lower left, a 10 per cent solution of NaCl; and in the lower right, mineral oil

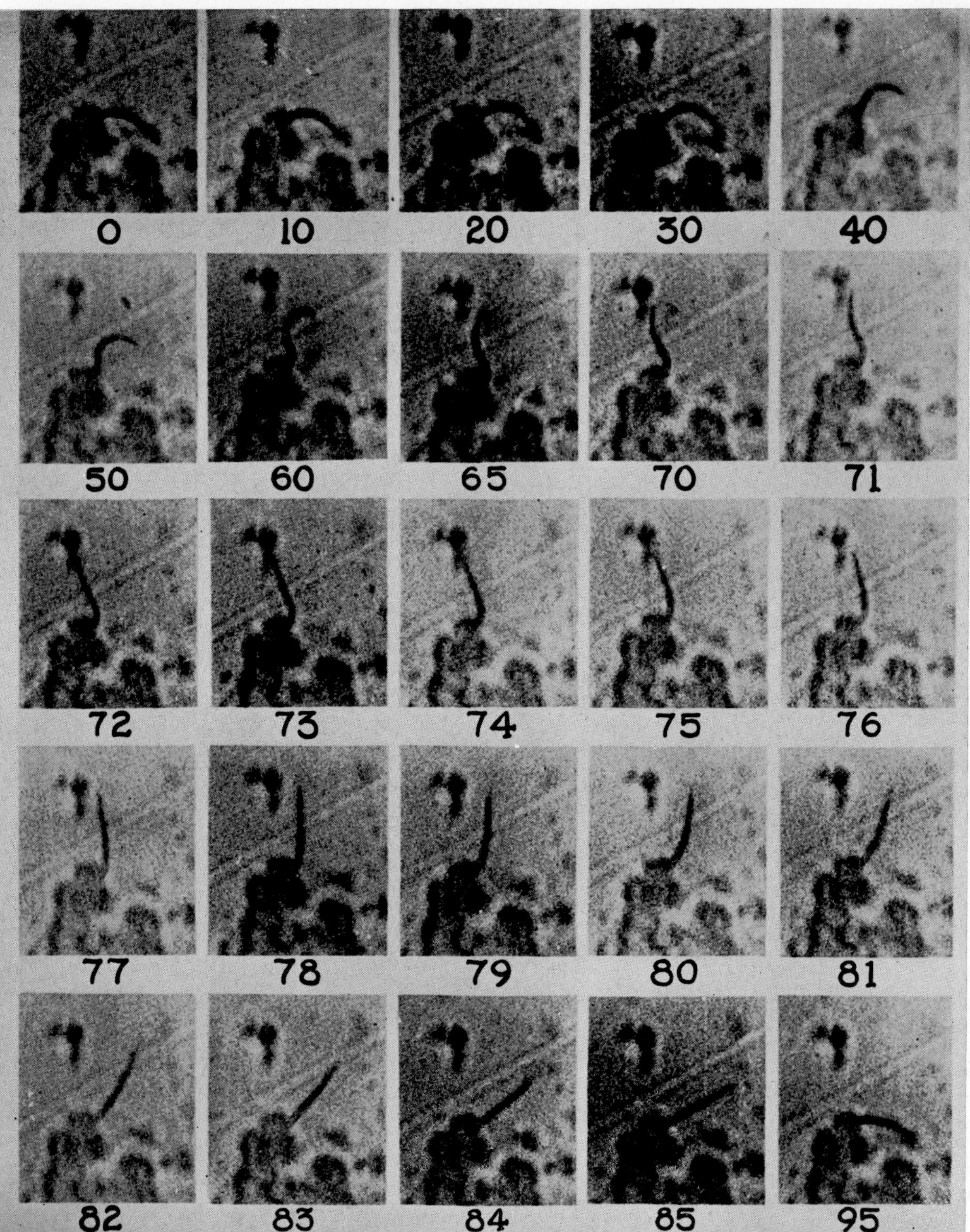

EVEN THE CLAM

High-speed photography is entering the field of microscopy and promises to be useful in biology.

As an early example, stages in the beat of a cilium from the gill of a clam (Mya) are shown above. The photographs are from consecutive photomicrographs (slightly retouched to give contrast) taken at intervals of 0.005 second. The numerals represent the number of time intervals. Magnification is 300. The pictures were taken for Dr. M. W. Jennison and Dr. J. W. M. Bunker

GRAPHICAL ANALYSIS OF MACHINE OPERATION

The automatic tapping machine at the left cuts threads at the high rate of 3,000 revolutions per minute, completing in 1.1 seconds the entire sequence of cutting a thread. On its drive shaft has been fixed a dial which was photographed with the high-speed motion-picture camera. From this record the entire action of the automatic chuck may be studied at will and reduced to the graphical analysis shown in the plot

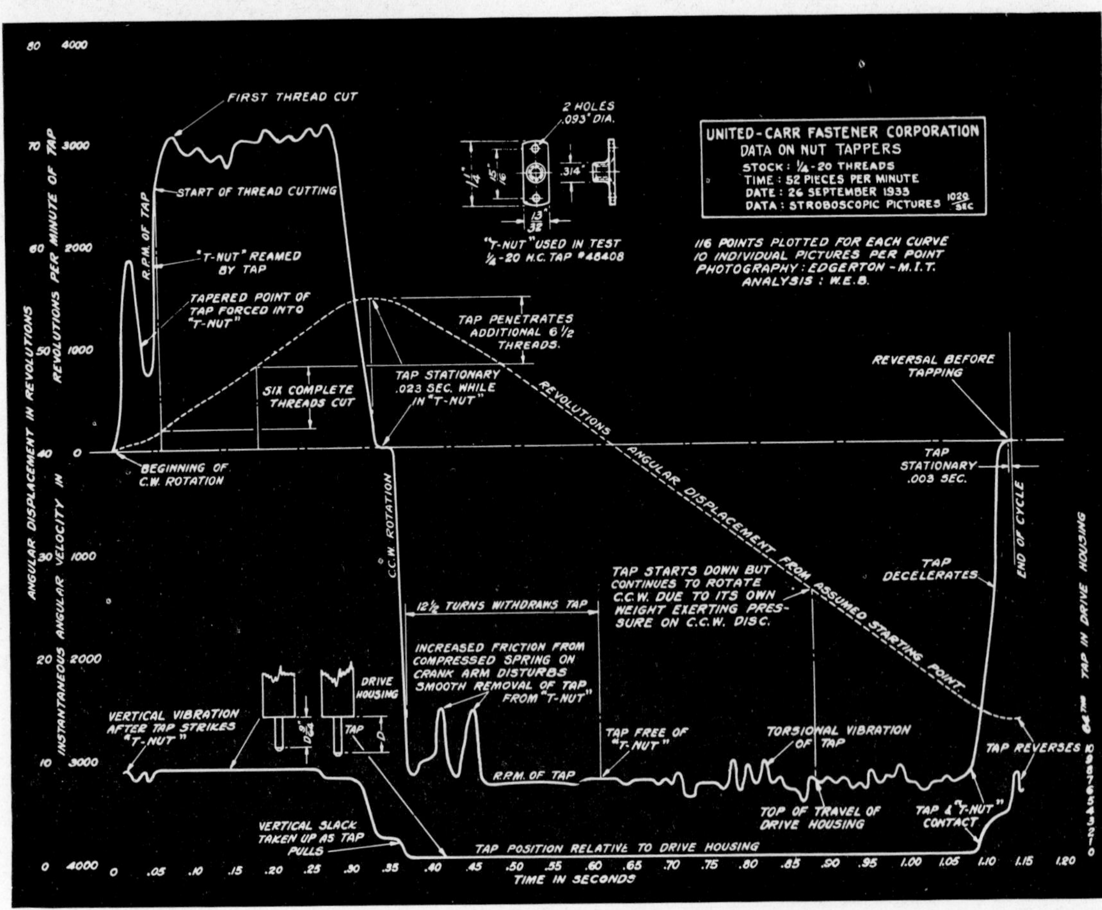

Upper right. In gear grinding, the grinding angle can be seen and the speed checked with the Strobotac

Upper left. The stroboscope is used to measure the speed of the fan, and to study air flow and its relation to the design of fans. Vibrations of the vanes are clearly seen

Lower left. On the differential analyzer at M.I.T., displacements as small as 1/10,000th of an inch are measured with the Strobotac

Lower right. Spindle-speed measurement and adjustment are made simple with the portable stroboscope

HIGH-SPEED OPERATIONS STAND STILL FOR OBSERVATION

Portable stroboscopes, as seen above, are used to study fast periodic motion by direct observation. The stroboscope completely removes the blur and brings out the moving element clearly and sharply, showing all the irregularities, distortion, and vibration present in the original motion. Just as it enables the camera to see high speed, so does it enable the eye to see.

PEOPLE IN ACTION

Above and opposite. Multiple-exposure photographs of children running. The above picture was taken at the rate of 10 exposures a second, the opposite pictures at the rate of 30 a second

GIRL SKIPPING ROPE

GIRL SKIPPING ROPE RUNNING

BOY JUMPING A LOW HURDLE
One hundred exposures a second

FANNING CARDS

Between hands, quicker than the eye, floats the ace of spades. Performed by Stephen G. Simpson

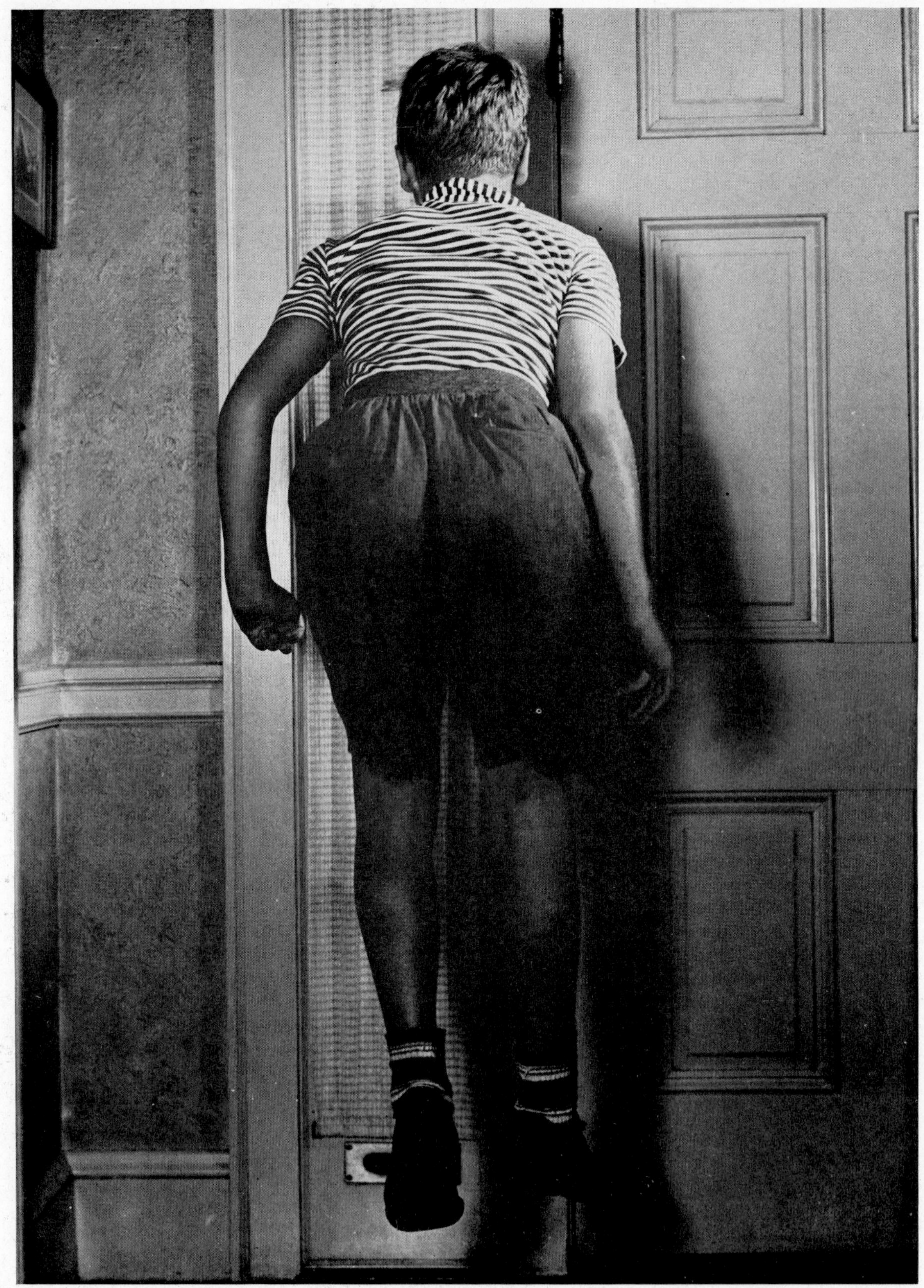

LEVITATION?

PLAY

FROZEN MOTION

Gjon Mili

FLOWING MOTION
Multiple-exposure sequence

JUMP!

Gjon Mili

THE DANCE — Gjon Mili

With stroboscopic lighting equipment the dance can now be photographed with adequate depth and detail

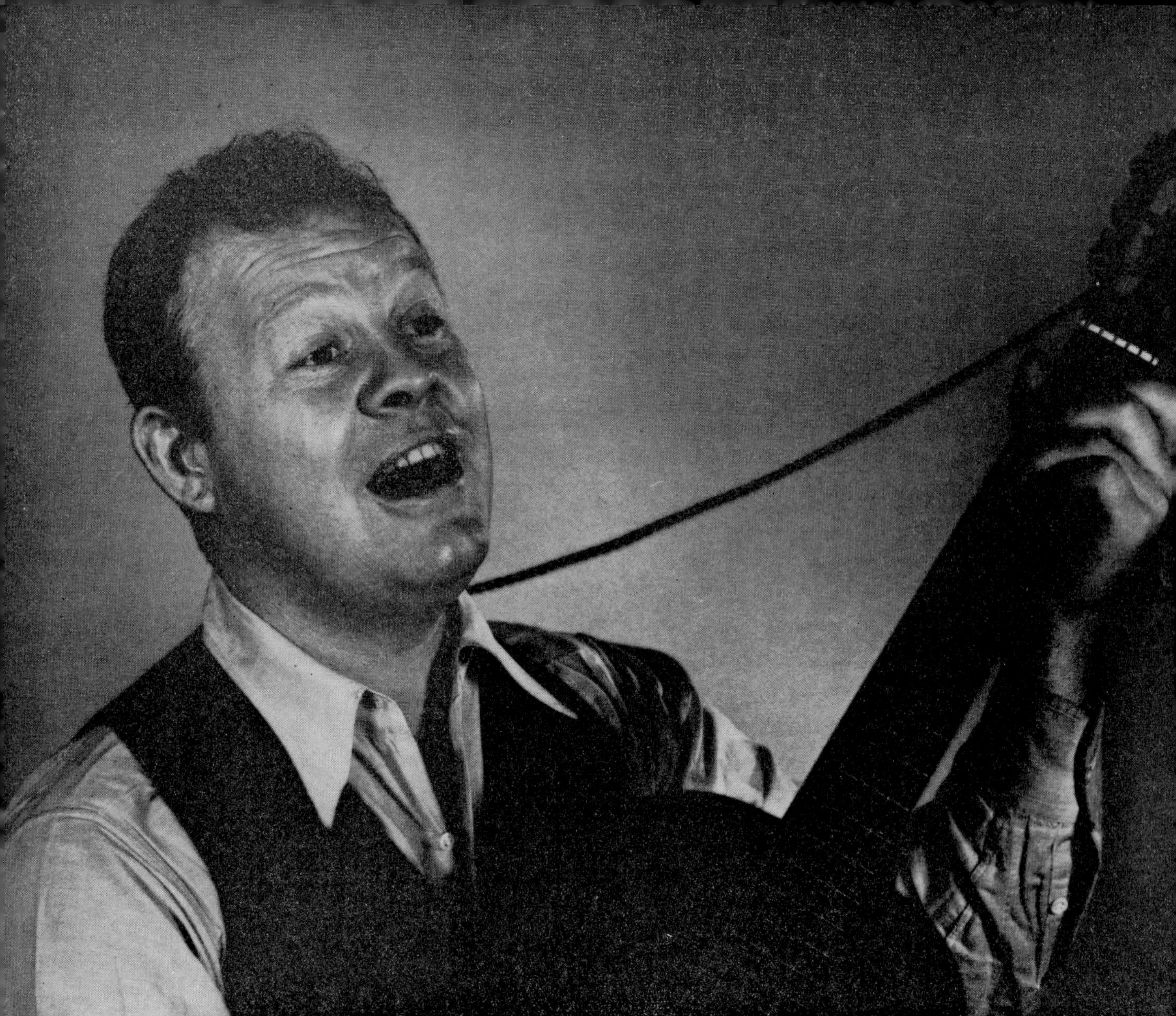

PORTRAITS

High-speed photography releases portraiture from the restrictions of slow exposure, the necessity of keeping the subject from moving. Perfectly natural, dynamic interpretations may be made without resorting to poses.

Gjon Mili, who took the adjacent pictures with the stroboscopic lights, is the first professional photographer to specialize in high-speed portraiture. Mili uses a duplex light source which combines an incandescent tungsten lamp, of sufficient intensity to facilitate light modeling and camera focusing without discomfort to the subject, and a flash tube so superimposed as to duplicate the lighting effect achieved with the tungsten lamp. The lighting system is synchronized with the camera so that the flash occurs at the point of maximum lens shutter opening.

The light available is sufficient to cover an area of 20 by 20 feet at **f**:11, while close-ups may be shot at apertures down to **f**:45.

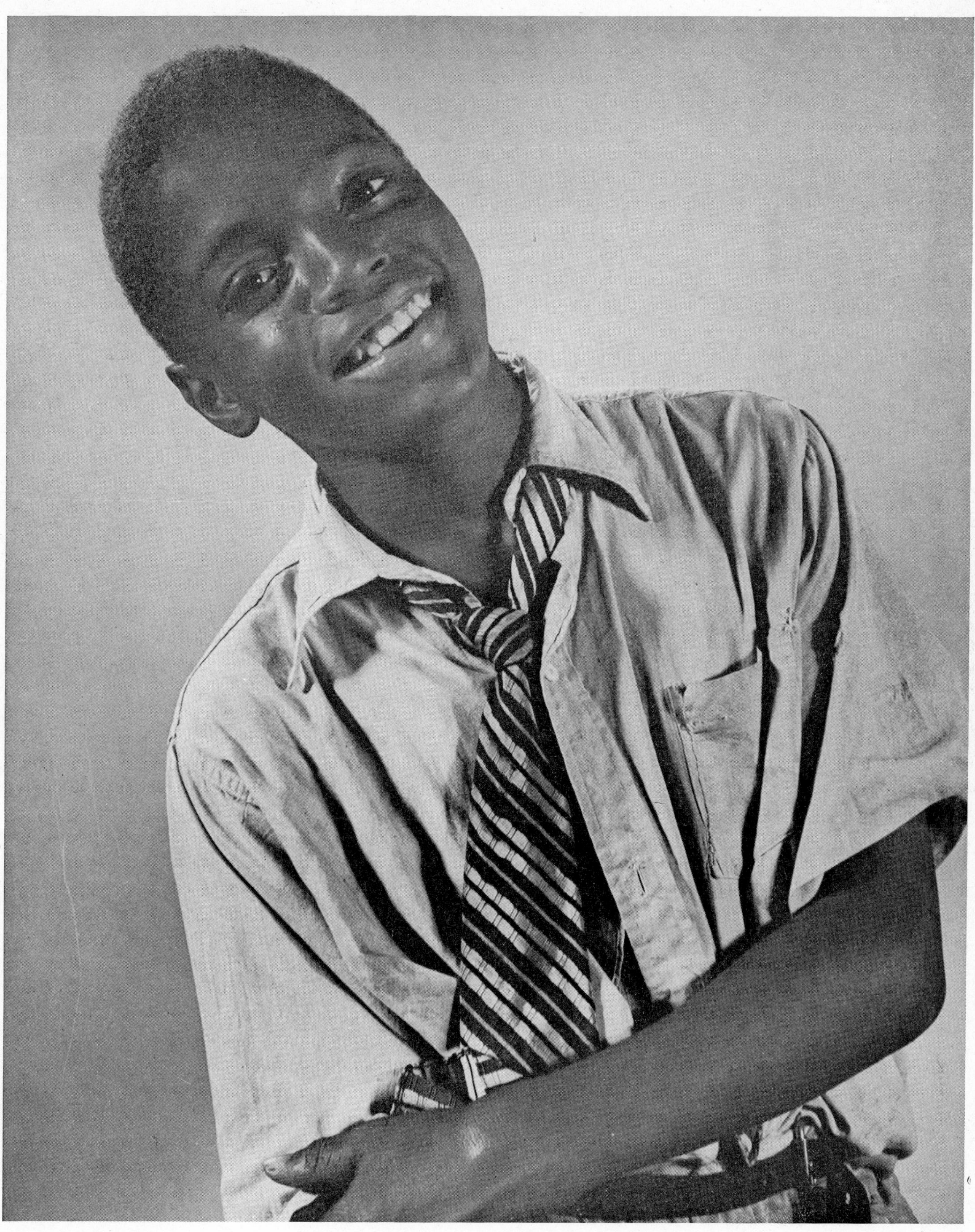

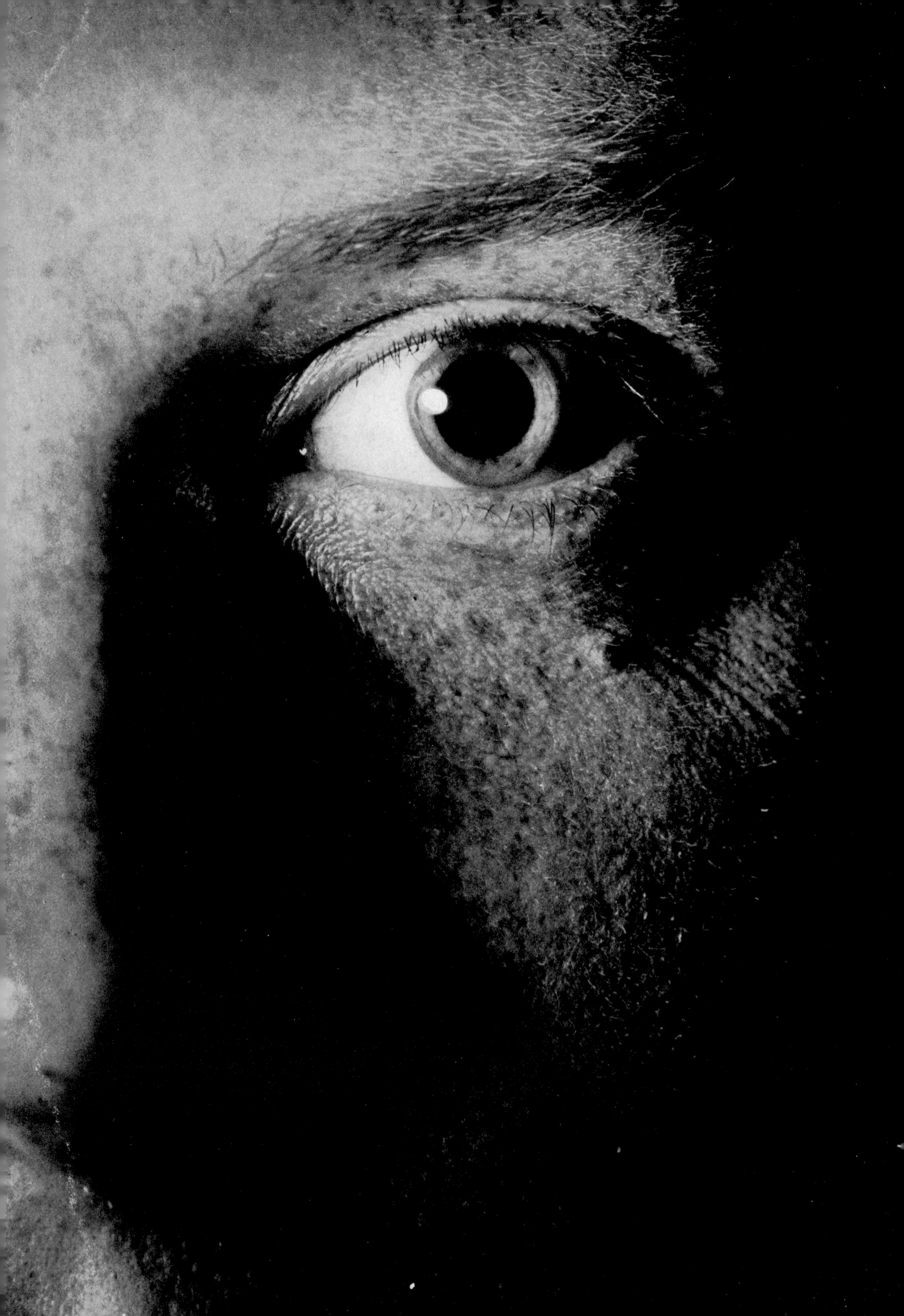

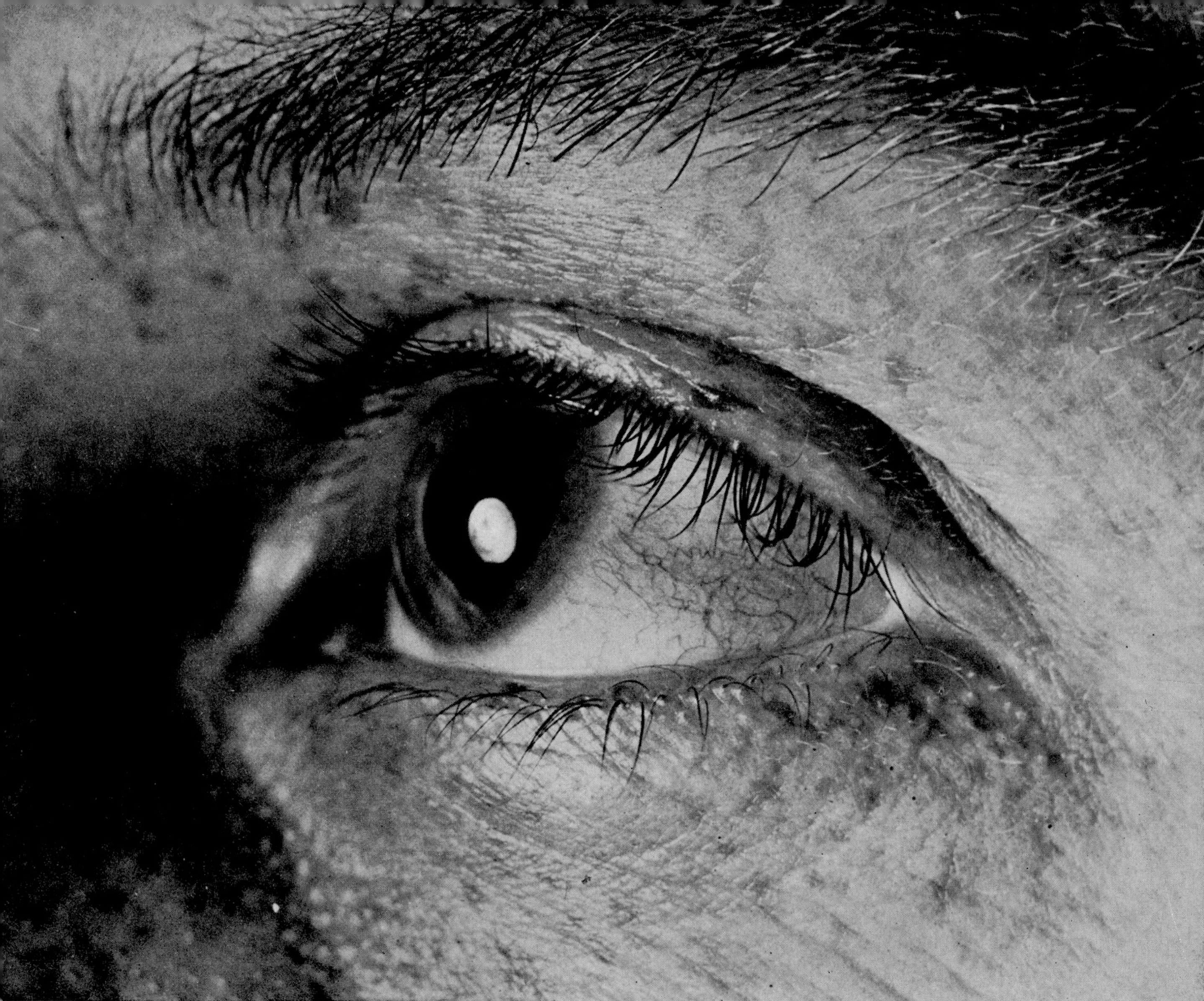

THE IRIS OF THE EYE

This eye had adjusted itself to total darkness when it was suddenly photographed by a single flash of light, catching the iris opened wide (see opposite). The actinic intensity of the light source is responsible for the startling detail. Note the blood vessels in the eye, the wirelike lashes, the texture of the skin. Here is a new degree of realism

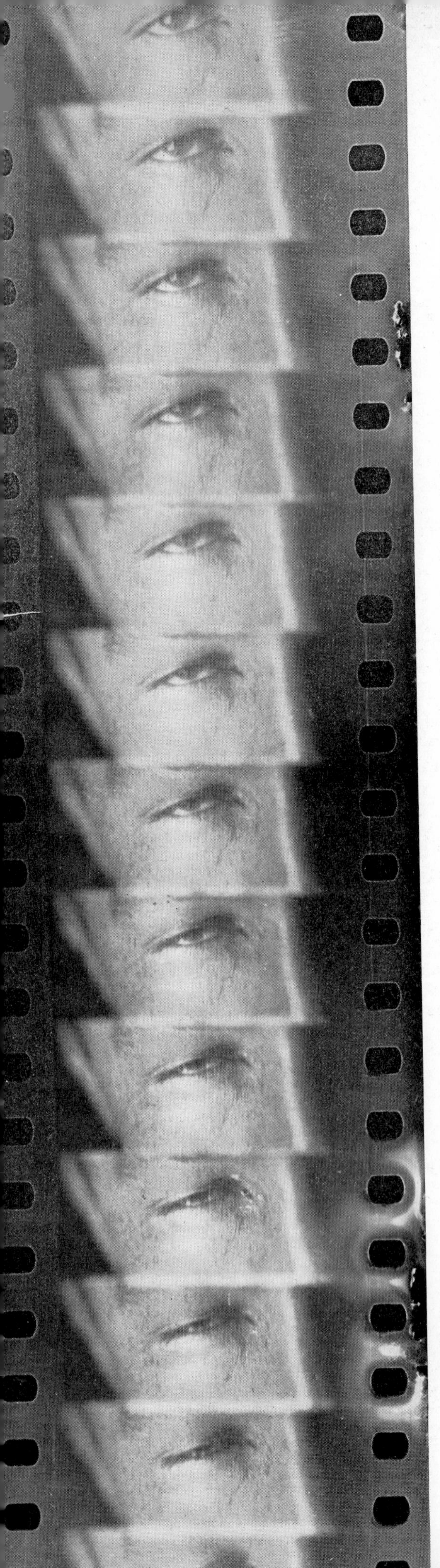

QUICK AS A WINK

How quick is a wink? Ultrahigh-speed motion-pictures supply the answer: about 1/40 of a second.
The excerpt shown was taken at the rate of 480 half frames a second on the first experimental stroboscopic motion-picture camera built at M.I.T.

FACES AND MUSCLES IN ACTION

Here are close-ups of bodies in action which show how high-speed photography achieves a candor beyond the reach of the ordinary candid camera. Too evanescent even for the observant eye are these fleeting grimaces on faces normally in controlled repose—the wry, tense, and sometimes agonized expressions that accompany rapid, intently co-ordinated, or strenuous action. Almost invariably the people who see their stroboscopic portraits are amazed or amused to see themselves as the high-speed camera sees them

JUJITSU — WITH EXPRESSION

The cat records alertness with grace; the schooling greyhound, visciousness with speed

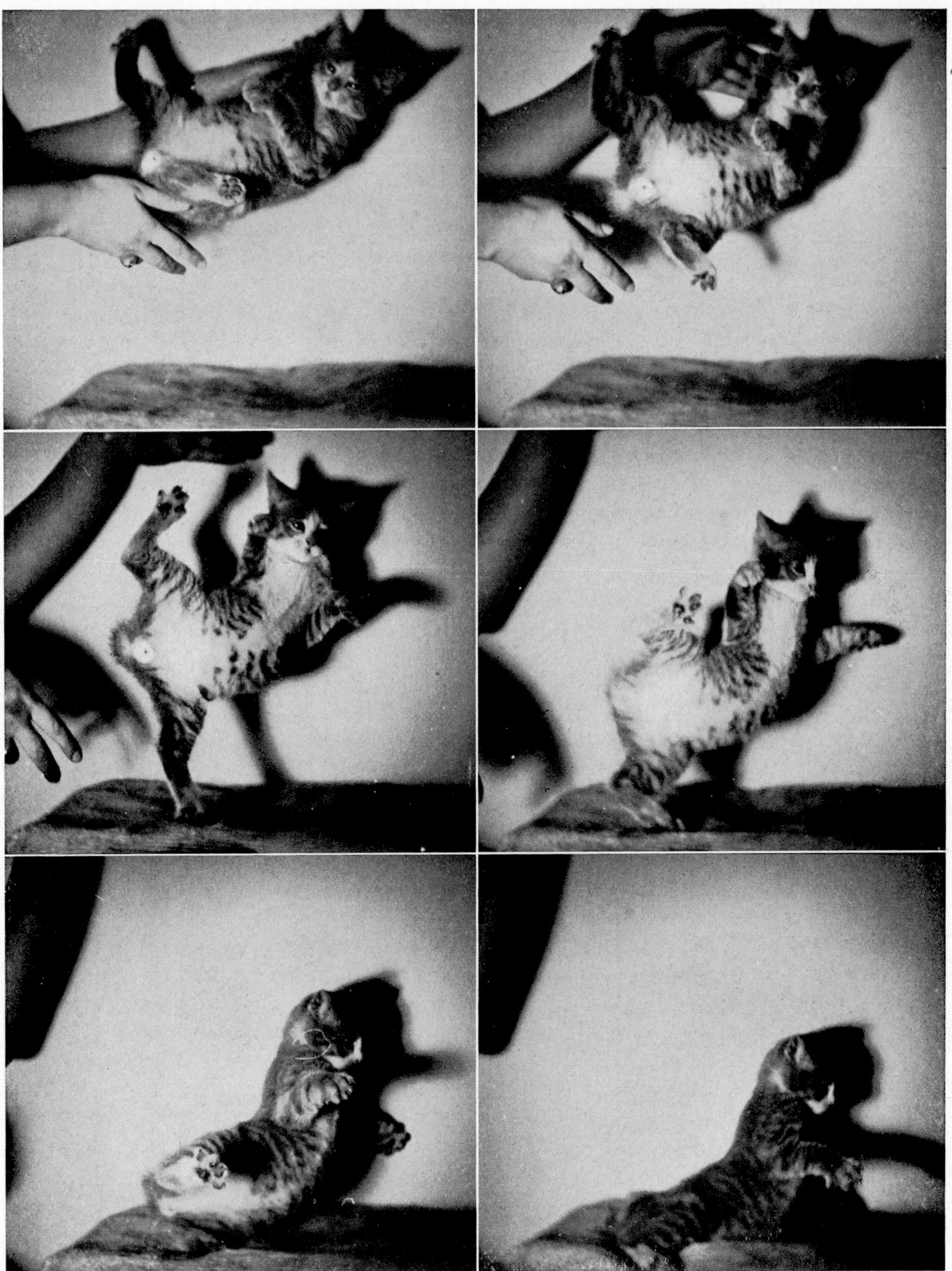

EVEN A TAILLESS CAT LANDS ON ITS FEET

The high-speed motion-picture camera verifies the age-old observation of the cat's reliable landing technique

PERFECT FORM

Gjon M

DOG AND MOUSE

Gjon Mi

SHOWER BATH — Gjon Mili

BEDTIME

DIRECTIONS FOR ASSEMBLING A SINGLE-LIGHT FLASH UNIT FOR HIGH-SPEED PHOTOGRAPHY

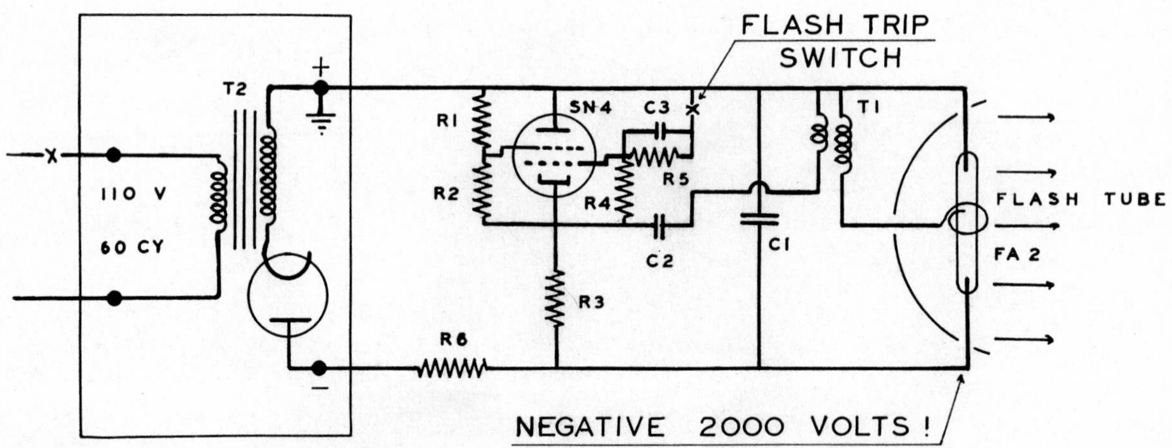

WIRING DIAGRAM OF A STROBOSCOPIC-LIGHT FLASH UNIT

IMPORTANT

Ground positive side of the circuit to a water pipe.
Insulate negative wiring for 2000 volts and cover so that the terminals cannot be touched.
Remember that the condenser C-1 holds a charge even after the main switch is open. Before changing tubes or working on circuit, be sure to short-circuit the condenser terminals.

It is possible for competent amateurs, particularly those expert in building radio equipment, to assemble a satisfactory light source for high-speed photography by following the directions given above. All the items in the parts list except the first three are available from radio supply houses.

Since dangerously high voltages are involved, as indicated on the wiring diagram, it is important for the builder and operator to know how to take the proper precautions.

PARTS LIST

For a Single-Light High-Speed Flash Unit

(Refer to Wiring Diagram)

Tubes: 1 Type FA2 argon flash tube (2000 v).
1 Type SN4 Strobotron tube.

T-1 Special high-ratio spark coil, 25-6000 turns
Above special items are available from Mr. K. J. Germeshausen, 84 Ellery St., Cambridge, Mass.

C-1 Main Flash Condenser.
The quantity of light and the duration of the flash are roughly proportional to the capacity. 100 microfarads will produce approximately half as much light as a small photo-flash lamp and have an effective duration of less than 100 microseconds. Any 2000-volt (d-c) condenser can be used in this service. Satisfactory photographs of small areas can be obtained with a capacitor of several microfarads.

T-2 Power supply transformer and rectifier tube to charge condenser C-1 to 2000 volts. Standard apparatus as used for cathode-ray and television tubes are suitable.

C-2 1-microfarad 400- volt condenser (paper).

C-3 0.01-microfarad 400-volt condenser (paper or mica).

R-1 125,000-ohm resistor, 2-watt.

R-2 25,000-ohm resistor, 2-watt.

R-3 1-megohm. (Use two 2-megohm resistors in parallel. I.R.C. Type FC-3, 3-watt. There is **high voltage** across this resistor. Insulate the high-potential end well.)

R-4 1-megohm, 2-watt.

R-5 1-megohm, 2-watt.

R-6 5000-ohm resistor, 10-watt.

ACKNOWLEDGMENTS

The development of stroboscopes and high-speed photography at the Massachusetts Institute of Technology has gone forward as a result of the efforts and interest of Kenneth J. Germeshausen and Herbert E. Grier, who have been associated with the work almost from the start. It is my pleasure here to acknowledge their full share in the developments and in the applications of those developments to practical uses. The technical skill of Germeshausen with intricate circuits and special tubes, and of Grier with complicated mechanical and electrical construction, played a large part in the program that has culminated in this book of pictures. Both Messrs. Germeshausen and Grier assisted in taking many of the photographs.

Throughout the high-speed program our work has been greatly stimulated by the astonishingly varied problems which have been brought to us. Industry particularly has provided opportunities for applying the high-speed technique, and the practical demands of industrial problems required us to take our equipment out of the laboratory and to adapt it to a workaday world. In this industrial work we have had the active assistance of Arthur D. Little, Inc., consulting engineers. The General Radio Company has made available to industry stroboscopic instruments and motion-picture cameras which we carried only through the laboratory stage of development.

In general the captions to the pictures in this book give credit, albeit inadequately, to those who helped in the taking of the pictures. These credit lines, however, need to be supplemented by the following notes on specific pictures:

Page	
27	Taken at the Austin Ornithological Station
28, 29	Homing pigeon lent by Dr. Eliot Hubbard, Jr.
36-39	William Tucker assisted with photography
46, 47	Edward Gladding lent guns and assisted in photography
57	Courtesy, Ethyl Gasoline Corporation
58, 59, 60, 61, 63, 64, 65, 66, 74, 75, 76, 77, 78, 79, 88	Courtesy, A. G. Spalding and Bros.
92, 93	Courtesy, **Life.** Photographed by Gjon Mili

98, 183	Posed by James V. Dotson
108, 109, 110	Posed by William M. Folberth
111, 112	Posed by George D. Cremer
122, 123, 124, 125, 126, 127	Joseph Keithley assisted with photography
128	Courtesy, Winchester Repeating Arms Company
129	Courtesy, **Fortune**
143	Courtesy, Professor Frank M. Lewis
148	Courtesy, Crompton & Knowles Loom Works
149	Courtesy, Inter City Airlines, Inc.
157 (left)	Gun furnished by J. Stevens Arms Company
162	Courtesy, United-Carr Fastener Company
163	Photographs, courtesy General Radio Company
174	Posed by Mary Ellen Goodman
184	Posed by Thomas Rawson, Jr.
186, 187	Messrs. Ito, Matsumoto, and Bartash performing
190	Courtesy, **Life**

HAROLD E. EDGERTON

SELECTED REFERENCES

While not intended to be exhaustive, the following bibliography is a comprehensive list of the most important publications relating to the observation and photography of objects moving at high speed. References documenting the history of high-speed photography and the analysis of motion are included along with the most useful literature on apparatus and methods. High-speed photography by intermittent light and speed pictures by moving optical systems are both covered. Here, then, is source material not only for those who desire technical information but for the many others who would know more of the absorbing story of how a new dimension has been added to vision.

HIGH-SPEED PHOTOGRAPHY

ELECTRICAL METHODS

ABRAHAM, H., BLOCH, E., AND BLOCH, L. "Sur la Cinématographie Ultrarapide." Comptes Rendus des Séances de L'Académie des Sciences, *169*:1031-1033 (1919).

Describes an oscillating spark light source that was used by L. Bull of the Marey Institute, Paris.

BOYS, C. V. "On Electric Spark Photographs; or, Photography of Flying Bullets, and so on, by the Light of the Electric Spark." Nature, *47*:415-421, 440-446 (1892-1893).

A method of photographing bullets in silhouette by a flash from a spark.

CRANZ, C. *Lehrbuch der Ballistik.* Volume III: *Experimentelle Ballistik,* Section 9. Berlin: Julius Springer, 1927.

EDGERTON, H. E. "Stroboscopic Moving Pictures." Electrical Engineering, *50*:327-329 (1931).

EDGERTON, H. E. "The Mercury Arc as a Source of Intermittent Light." Journal of the Society of Motion Picture Engineers, *16*:735-741 (1931).

EDGERTON, H. E., AND GERMESHAUSEN, K. J. "Stroboscopic Photography." Electronics, *45*:220-221 (July, 1932).

EDGERTON, H. E. "Stroboscopic and Slow-Motion Moving Pictures by Means of Intermittent Light." Journal of the Society of Motion Picture Engineers, *18*:356-364 (1932).

EDGERTON, H. E., AND GERMESHAUSEN, K. J. "The Stroboscope and High-Speed Motion-Picture Camera as Research Instruments." Transactions of the American Institute of Chemical Engineers, *30*:420-437 (1933-1934).

EDGERTON, H. E., AND GERMESHAUSEN, K. J. "Stroboscopic-Light High-Speed Motion Pictures." Journal of the Society of Motion Picture Engineers, *23*:284-298 (1934).

EDGERTON, H. E. "High Speed Motion Pictures." Transactions of the American Institute of Electrical Engineers, *54*:149-153 (1935).

EDGERTON, H. E., GERMESHAUSEN, K. J., AND GRIER, H. E. "High-Speed Photography." Photographic Journal of Royal Photographic Society of Great Britain, *76*:198-204 (1936).

EDGERTON, H. E., GERMESHAUSEN, K. J., AND GRIER, H. E. "High Speed Photographic Methods of Measurement." Journal of Applied Physics, *8*:2-9 (1937).

EDGERTON, H. E., GERMESHAUSEN, K. J., AND GRIER, H. E. "Multiflash Photography." Photo technique, *1*:No. *5*:14-16 (Oct., 1939).

GLATZEL, BRUNO. *Elektrische Methoden der Momentphotographie.* Braunschweig: Friedr. Vieweg und Sohn (1915).

HARVEY, E. NEWTON, AND LOOMIS, ALFRED L. "High Speed Photomicrography of Living Cells Subjected to Supersonic Vibrations." Journal of General Physiology, *15*:147-153 (1931).

MAREY, E. J. *Animal Mechanism.* New York: D. Appleton (1893).

MAREY, E. J. *Movement.* Translated by Eric Pritchard. New York: D. Appleton (1895).

QUAYLE, PHILIP P. "Spark Photography and its Application to Some Problems in Ballistics." Scientific Papers of the Bureau of Standards, Number 508 (June 15, 1925).

ROTHROCK, A. M. "The N.A.C.A. Apparatus for Studying the Formation and Combustion of Fuel Sprays and the Results from Preliminary Tests." National Advisory Committee for Aeronautics Report Number 429 (1932).

SCHARDIN, HUBERT. "Beschutz von Drähten und Panzerplatten." Veröffentlichung der Reichsstelle für den Unterrichtsfilm zu dem Hochschulfilm Nr. C 142.

SCHARDIN, HUBERT. "Die Verfahren der Funkenkinematographie." Beiträge zur Ballistik und technischen Physik. Leipzig: Johann Ambrosius Barth (1938).

SCHARDIN, HUBERT, UND STRUTH, W. "Neuere Ergebnisse der Funkenkinematographie." Zeitschrift für technische Physik, *18*:474-477 (1937).

SCHARDIN, HUBERT, UNTER MITARBEIT VON STRUTH, W., UND WOEHL, W. "Dum-Dum-Wirkung." Veröffentlichung der Reichsstelle für den Unterrichtsfilm zu dem Hochschulfilm Nr. C 229.

SEGUIN, AUGUSTIN. "Les Appareils Stroborama et Leurs Applications." Bulletin de la Société Française des Électriciens, Cinquième Série, *4*:405-412 (1934).

TALBOT, WILLIAM HENRY FOX. The British Journal of Photography, *11*:340-341 (1864).

TALBOT, WILLIAM HENRY FOX. Spark photography patent. Number 13,664, Specifications of Inventions, June 12, 1851.
"Calotype Process, Inventor of the." The Photographic News, *21*:474-475 (1877).
An account of Talbot's pioneer work.

TAYLOR, H. G. AND WALDRAM, J. M. "Improvements in the Schlieren Method." Journal of Scientific Instruments, *10*:378-389 (1933).
This article contains a comprehensive bibliography of the Schlieren method, including several papers on spark sources as used in this method of making silhouette photographs.

TOWNEND, H. C. H. "Improvements in the Schlieren Method of Photography." Journal of Scientific Instruments, *11*:184-187 (1934).

WITHROW, LLOYD, AND RASSWEILER, GERALD M. "Studying Engine Combustion by Physical Methods." Journal of Applied Physics, *9*:362-372 (1938).
Description of use of multiple-flash apparatus in the laboratories of the National Advisory Committee for Aeronautics, Langley Field, Va.

WORTHINGTON, A. M. *A Study of Splashes.* New York: Longmans Green (1908).

This book is a summary of the beautiful experimental researches of Professor Worthington. He made the first extensive use of single-flash photography by reflected light and showed ingenuity in the development of timing methods.

OPTICAL METHODS

"AEG-ZEITDEHNER, DER." AEG-Mitteilungen, November, 1933.

Rotating lenses and slits are used to stop the motion of the image with respect to the film.

ENDE, W. "Theorie des Thunschen Zeitdehners und ihre Anwendung in der Aufnahmepraxis." Zeitschrift für technische Physik, *11*:394-402 (1930).

FRASER, REGINALD P. "The Photography of Flame in Gaseous Explosions." The Photographic Journal, *74*:388-405 (1934).

"Heape and Grylls Machine for High Speed Photography, The." Journal of Scientific Instruments, *4*:82-87 (1926).

See also U. S. Patent 1,488,542. This camera, which used a rotating lens system similar to that used by Jenkins, took stereoscopic motion pictures at 5,000 frames per second on 35-millimeter film. The camera weighs several tons.

HERRIOTT, W. "High Speed Motion Picture Photography." The Bell System Technical Journal, *17*:393-405 (1938).

JENKINS, C. FRANCIS. "The Chronoteine Camera." Journal of the Society of Automotive Engineers, *22*:200-202 (1928).

JENKINS, C. FRANCIS. "The Jenkins Chronoteine Camera for High Speed Motion Studies." Transactions of the Society of Motion Picture Engineers, *25*:25-30 (1926).

A camera having 48 matched lenses in a gear-driven wheel is described. This camera is now at the Massachusetts Institute of Technology.

LEGG, J. W. "The Polar, Multi-Exposure, High Speed Camera." Electric Journal, *16*:509-512 (1919).

A limited number of photographs are taken simultaneously by a multisectioned shutter wheel and a number of lenses. The film in this camera is stationary.

MAGNAN, ANTOINE. *La Locomotion chez les Animaux.* I. *Le Vol des Insectes.* Paris: Hermann (1934).

PRINCE, D. C. AND RANKIN, W. K. "A 120,000 Exposure per Second Camera," General Electric Review, *42*:391-393 (Sept., 1939).

SUHARA, TOYOTARO; SATO, NAOZO; AND KAMEI, SIDUTAKE. "A New Ultra-Speed Kinematographic Camera Taking 40,000 Photographs per Second." Reports of the Aeronautical Research Institute, Tôkyô Imperial University, *5*:187-194 (1930).

Optical correction for the continuously moving film is made by means of a gear-driven multisided mirror. This camera weighs several tons. A more recent model is reported to have achieved a speed of 80,000 pictures a second.

THOMPSON, L., AND RIFFOLT, U. "Ballistic Engineering Problems: Experimental Development." Proceedings of the U. S. Naval Institute, *58*:377-393 (1932).

THUN, RUDOLPH. "Fortschritte der Hochfrequenz-Kinematographie." Zeitschrift des Vereines Deutscher Ingenieure, *82*:697-700 (1938).

TUTTLE, F. E. "A Non-intermittent High-Speed 16-mm Camera." Journal of the Society of Motion Picture Engineers, *21*:474-477 (1933).

A rotating plane prism is used to stop the image on the continuously moving film.

BARSTOW, F. E., AND EDGERTON, H. E. "Glass Fracture Velocity." Journal of the American Ceramic Society (article to be published shortly).

EDGERTON, H. E., HAUSER, E. A., HOLT, B. M., AND COX, J. T., JR. "The Application of the High-Speed Motion Picture Camera to Research on the Surface Tension of Liquids." Journal of Physical Chemistry, *40*:973-988 (1936).

HAUSER, E. A. TUCKER, W. B., AND EDGERTON, H. E. "Studies in Drop Formation as Revealed by the High-Speed Motion Camera." Journal of Physical Chemistry, *41*:1017-1028 (1937).

MOORE, PAUL. "Vocal Fold Movement During Vocalization." Speech Monographs, December, 1937, page 44.

MUYBRIDGE, EADWEARD. *Animals in Motion.* London: Chapman and Hall (1899).

ŒHMICHEN, ETIENNE. *Nos Maîtres Les Oiseaux.* Paris: Dunod (1920).

SACO-LOWELL BULLETIN. "A Drafting Research by Means of High-Speed Photography." *8*:18-21 (October, 1936). Published by Saco-Lowell Shops, 147 Milk Street, Boston, Mass.

THE STROBOSCOPE

BAHLS, W. ENDRES, AND KNOWLES, D. D. "The Stroboglow." Electric Journal, *28*:250-253 (1931).

CHADWICK, LEIGH E. "A Simple Stroboscopic Method for the Study of Insect Flight." Psyche, *46*:1-8 (1939).

CHADWICK, LEIGH E. "Some Factors which Affect the Rate of Movement of the Wings in Drosophila." Physiological Zoology, April, 1939.

CROWLEY, J. F. "Intermittent Illumination in Industry, with Special Reference to Its Use for the Examination of Moving Bodies." The Illuminating Engineer, *16*:189-211 (1923). An excellent review of stroboscopic developments up to 1923.

DEJUHASZ, K. J. AND YOUNG, N. JR. "Stroboscope at Work in Automobile Research," Automotive Industries, *74*:660 and 690 (May 9 and 16, 1936).

DREWELL, P. "Methoden der technischen Stroboskopie." Jahrbuch des Forschungs-Instituts der Allgemeinen Elektricitäts-Gesellschaft, Fünfter Band, 1936-1937. Berlin: Julius Springer, 1938.

EDGERTON, H. E. "Study of the Flow of Air with a Stroboscope." Mechanical Engineering, *57*:228 (1935).

EDGERTON, H. E. AND GERMESHAUSEN, K. J. "The Mercury Arc as an Actinic Stroboscopic Light Source." Review of Scientific Instruments, *3*:535-542 (1932).

GENERAL RADIO EXPERIMENTER. "A New Stroboscope for Speed Measurements." *10*:1-3 (August, 1935). (See also current catalogues of the General Radio Company, Cambridge, Mass., for descriptions of commercially available stroboscopes and high-speed motion-picture apparatus.)

GENERAL RADIO EXPERIMENTER. "The Stroboscope." Volume 7, No. 7 (December, 1932).

GERMESHAUSEN, K. J., AND EDGERTON, H. E. "A Cold-Cathode Arc-Discharge Tube." Electrical Engineering, *55*:790*ff* (1936). (The tube described in this article is called a strobotron. It is used in a stroboscope manufactured by the General Radio Company of Cambridge, Mass., under the trade name of Strobotac.)

Germeshausen, K. J., and Edgerton, H. E. "The Strobotron." Electronics, *10*:12-14 (February, 1937).

Hitchcock, R. C. "Studying Parts in Motion with the New Stroboglow." Electric Journal, *32*:529-532 (1935).

Hopwood, Henry V. Living Pictures. London: Hatton Press (1915).

Moore, Paul. "A Short History of Laryngeal Investigation." The Quarterly Journal of Speech, *23*:531-564 (1937).

An excellent review of the development of stroboscopes, both optical and electrical.

Railsback, O. L. "Chromatic Stroboscopes," Acoustical Soc. America Journal, *9*:37-39 (July, 1937).

Ramsaye, Terry. "A Million and One Nights: A History of the Motion Picture." Volume I. New York: Simon and Schuster (1926).

de Stefanis, M. "Misure Stroboscopische," Elettrotechnica, *22*:802-804 (Dec. 10, 1935).

White, A. B., Nottingham, W. B., Germeshausen, K. J., and Edgerton, H. E. "The Strobotron—II" Electronics, *10*:18-21 (March, 1937).

Young, R. W. and Loomis, A. "Theory of Chromatic Stroboscope," Acoustical Soc. America Journal, *10*:112-116 (Oct., 1938).

Moore, Paul. "A Short History of Laryngeal Investigation." The Quarterly Journal of Speech, *23*:531-564 (1937).

An excellent review of the development of stroboscopes, both optical and electrical.

Ramsaye, Terry. *A Million and One Nights: A History of the Motion Picture.* Volume I. New York: Simon and Schuster (1926).